Amazing Dot-to-Dot

FOR GROWN-UPS

DAVID WOODROFFE

ARCTURUS

ARCTURUS

This edition published in 2015 by Arcturus Publishing Limited
26/27 Bickels Yard, 151–153 Bermondsey Street,
London SE1 3HA

ISBN: 978-1-78404-612-5
AD004569NT

Printed in China

Contents

Introduction 4

THE ANIMAL KINGDOM 7

LANDMARKS 16

ICONIC BUILDINGS 29

WORKS OF ART 51

ENTERTAINMENT 62

SPORT 76

AIR, LAND AND SEA 92

SCENES 110

List of illustrations 128

Introduction

This enjoyable cornucopia of unjoined dots is just waiting to be connected by someone with limitless patience, a sharp pencil and an eraser. Here's your chance.

Starting at dot number one (and you've got to find that first), join them up in sequence to uncover famous works of art and scenes from the worlds of entertainment, sport, transport and nature. So get your pencil and a straight edge and join the dots on each page to reveal a picture.

And we've supplied a list at the back of the book in case you can't put a name to the image you've exposed.

Here's a small one just to warm you up, followed by a more substantial challenge.

David Woodroffe

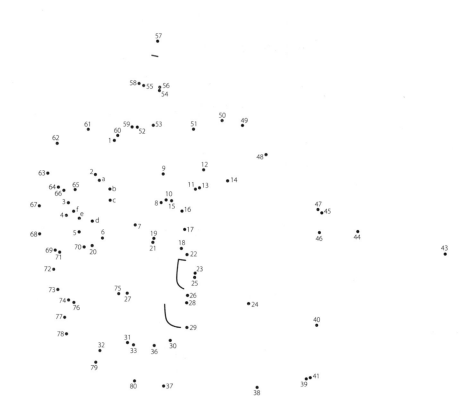

This picture is made from 2 continuous lines:
a) numbers and b) lower case letters

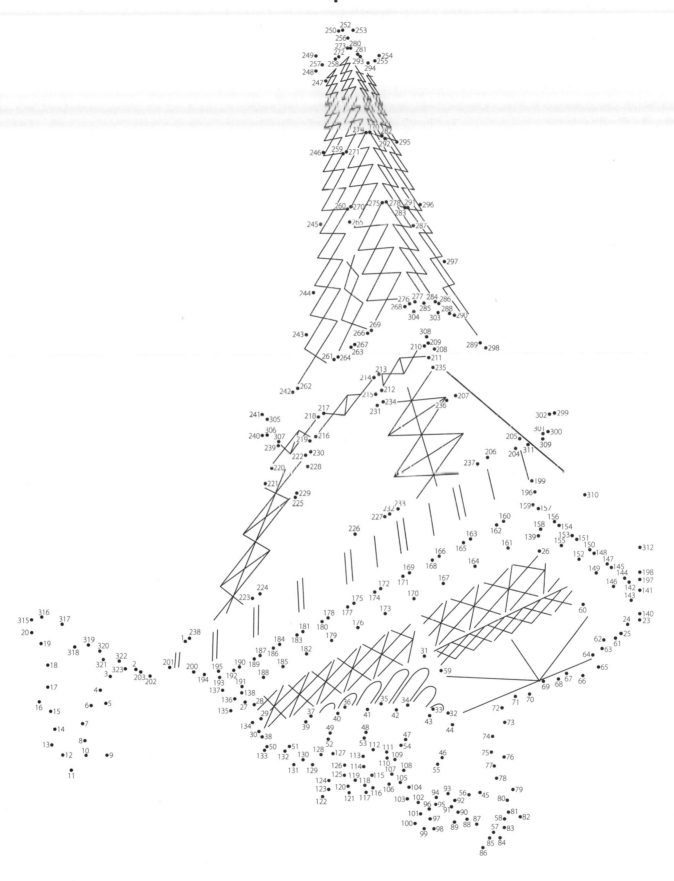

7

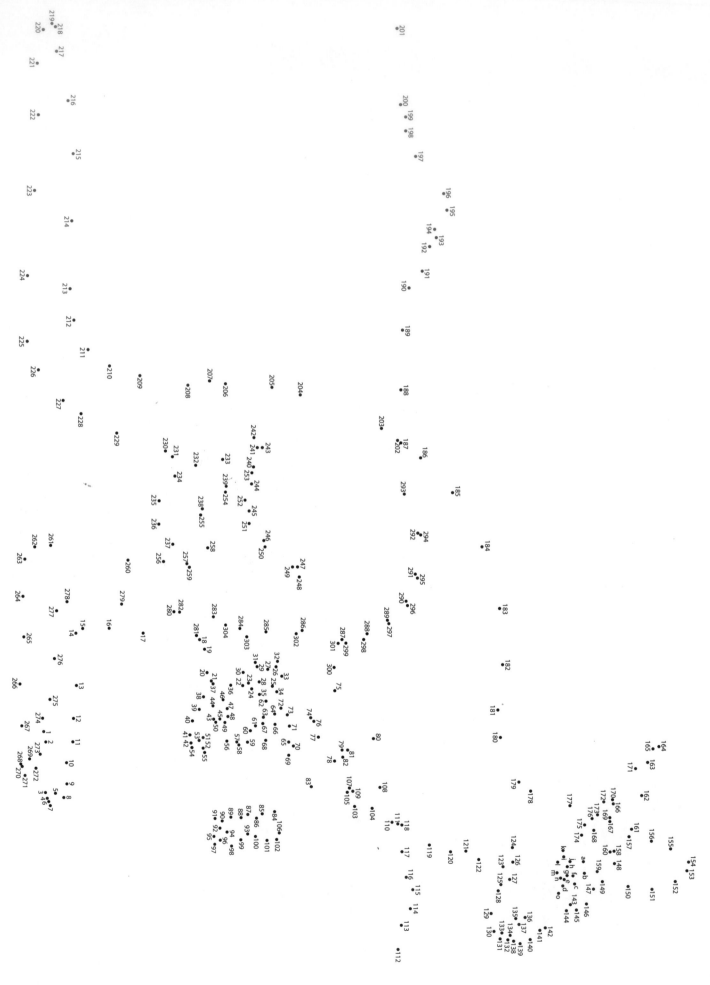

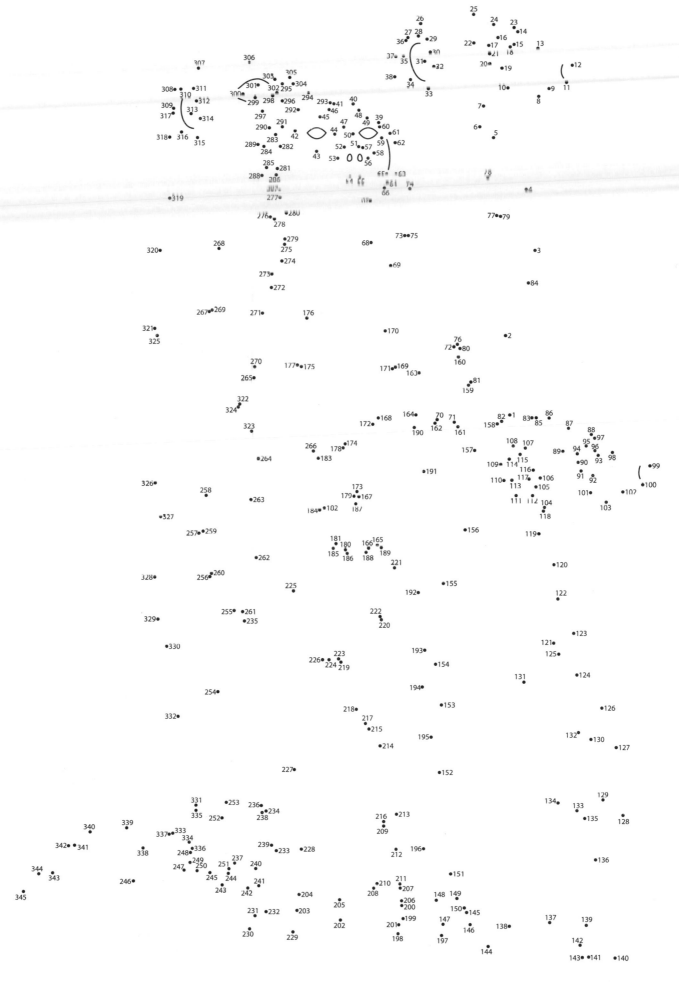

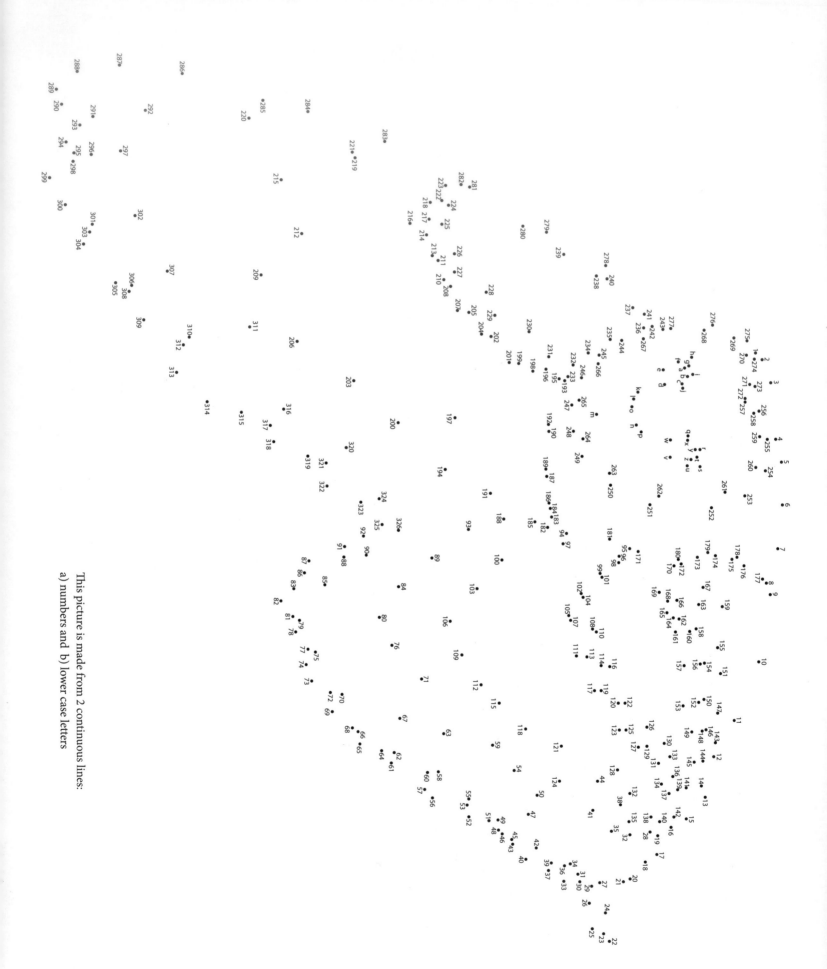

This picture is made from 2 continuous lines:
a) numbers and b) lower case letters

10

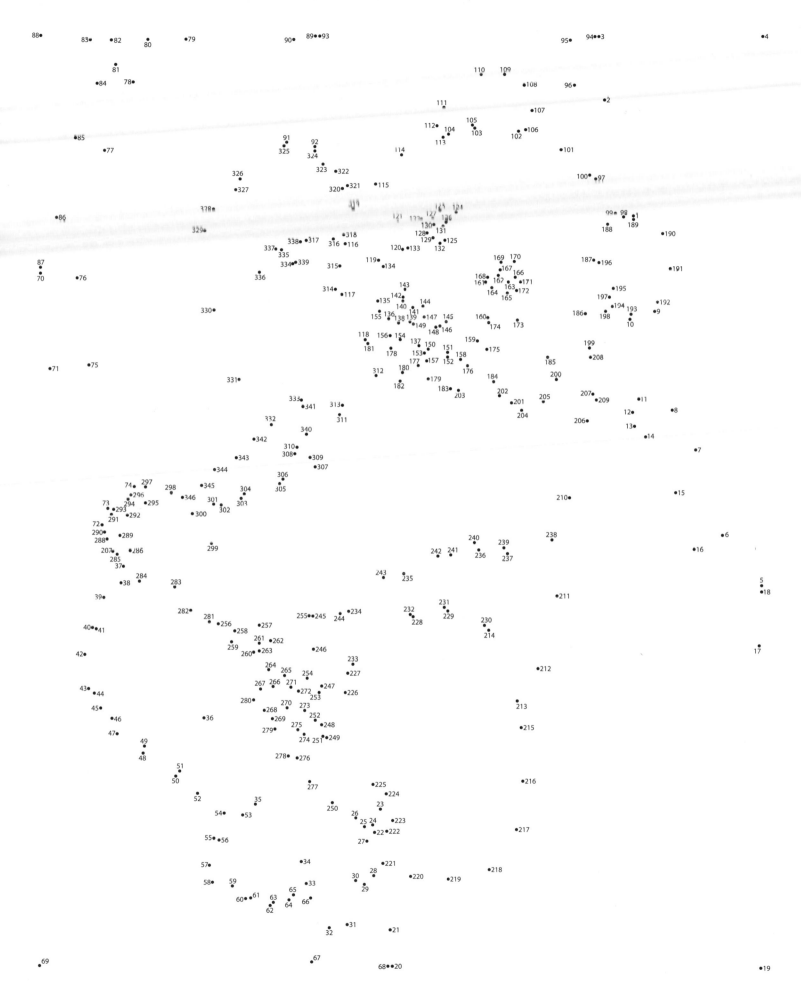

This picture is made from 4 continuous lines:
a) numbers, b) upper case letters, c) lower case letters and d) roman numerals

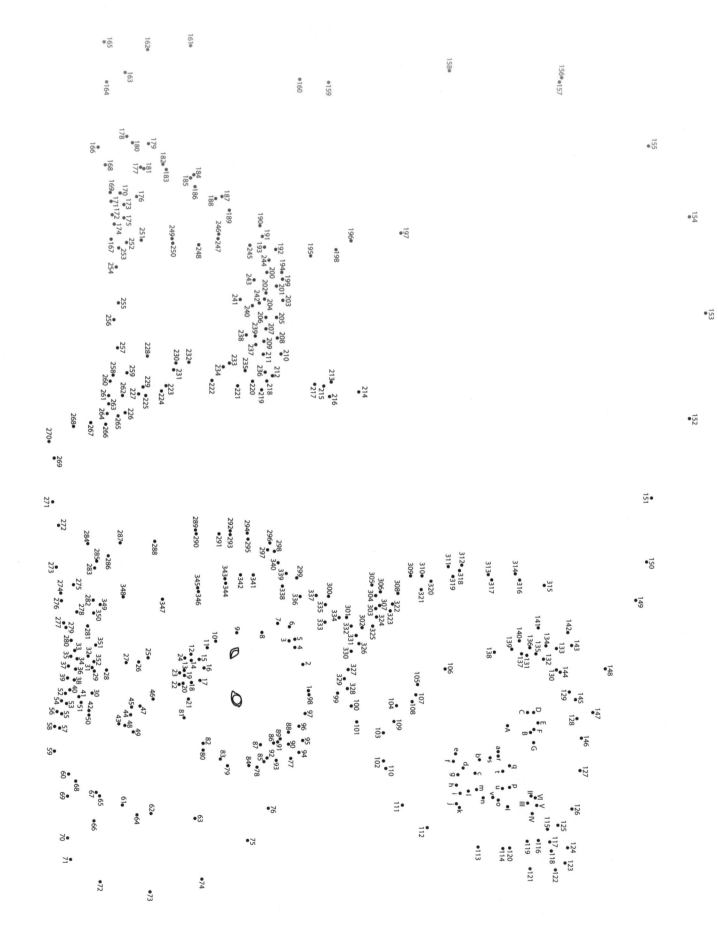

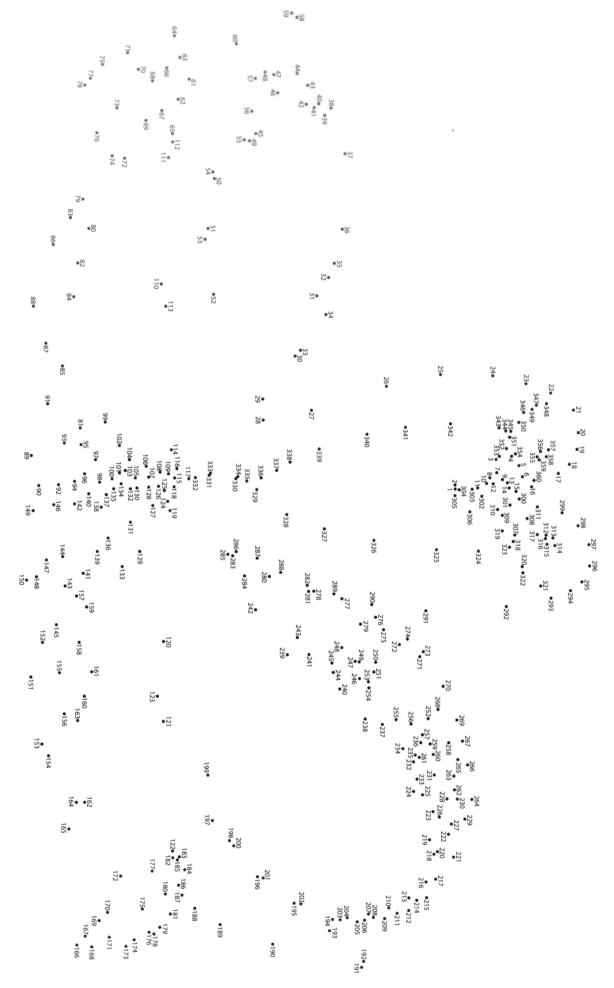

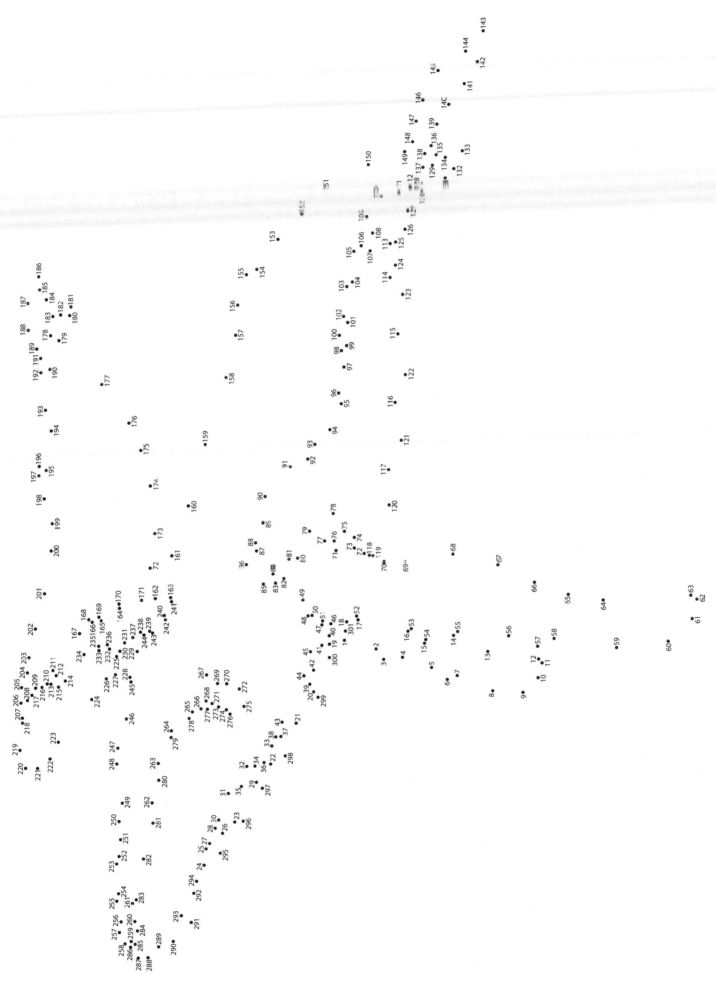

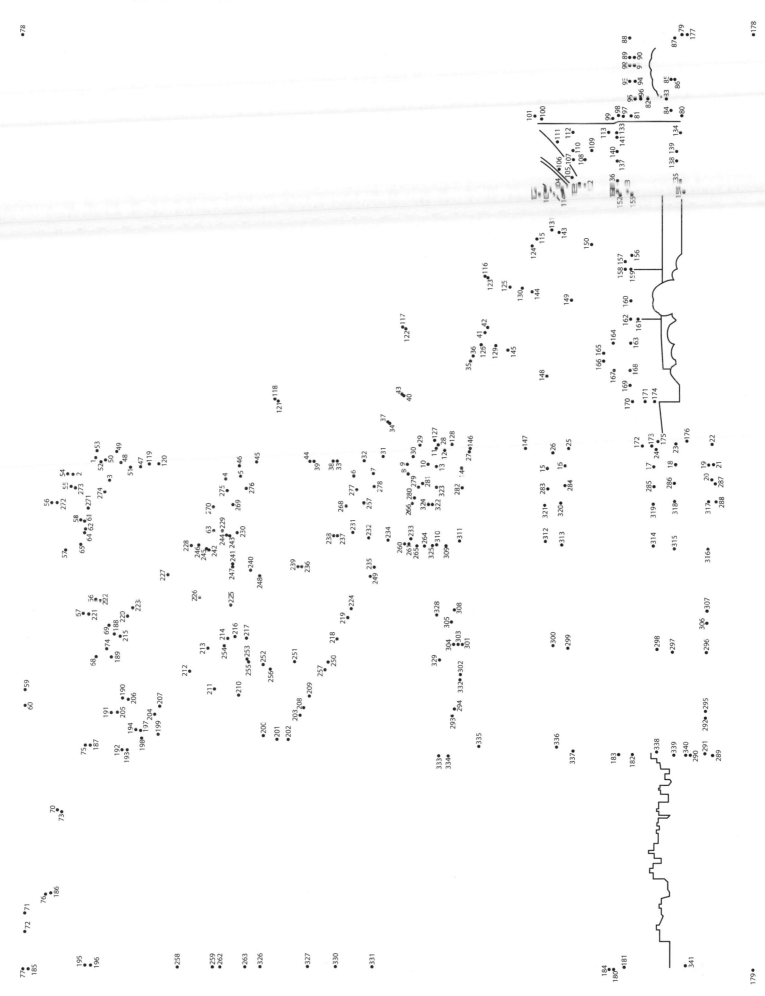

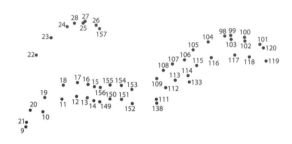
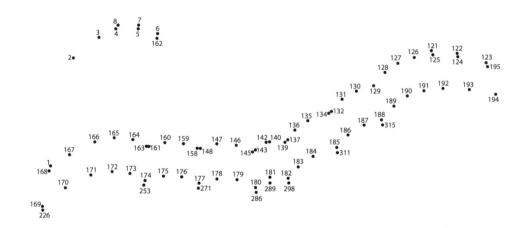
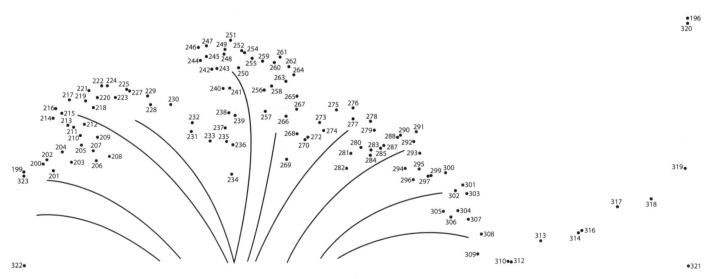

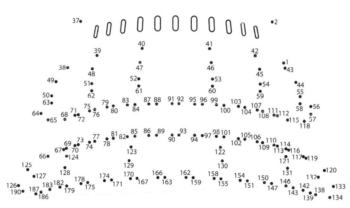
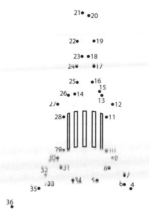
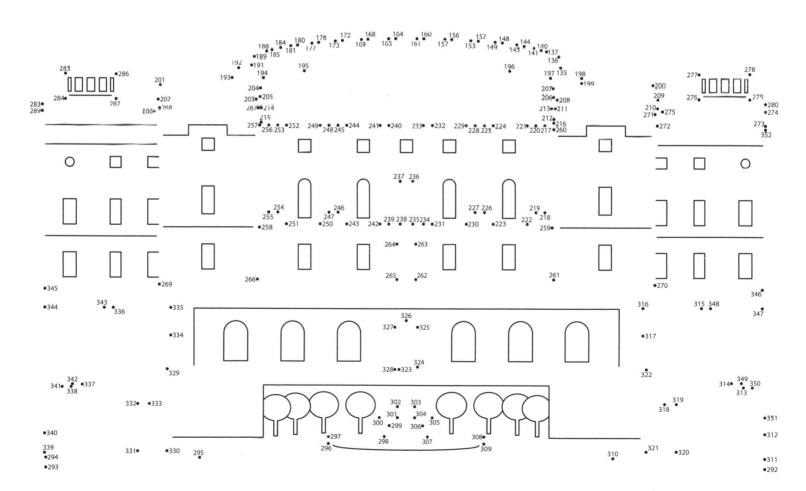

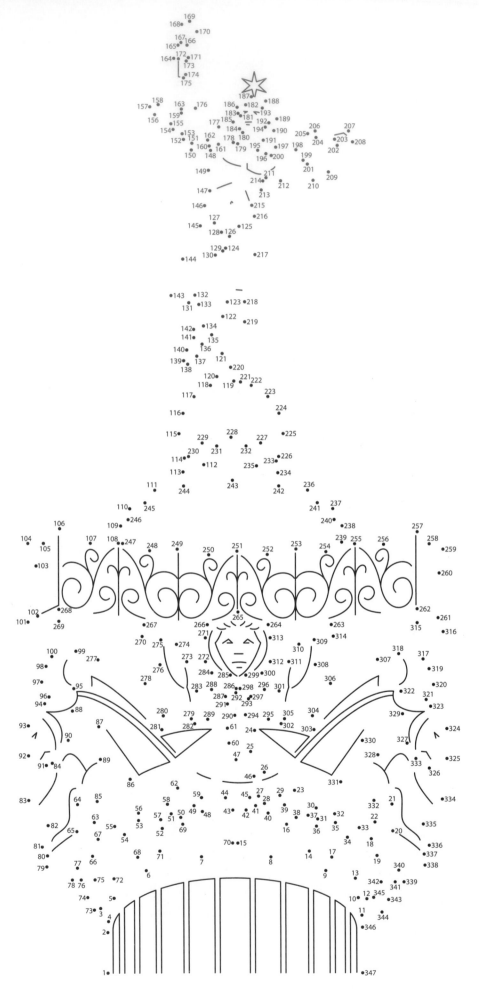

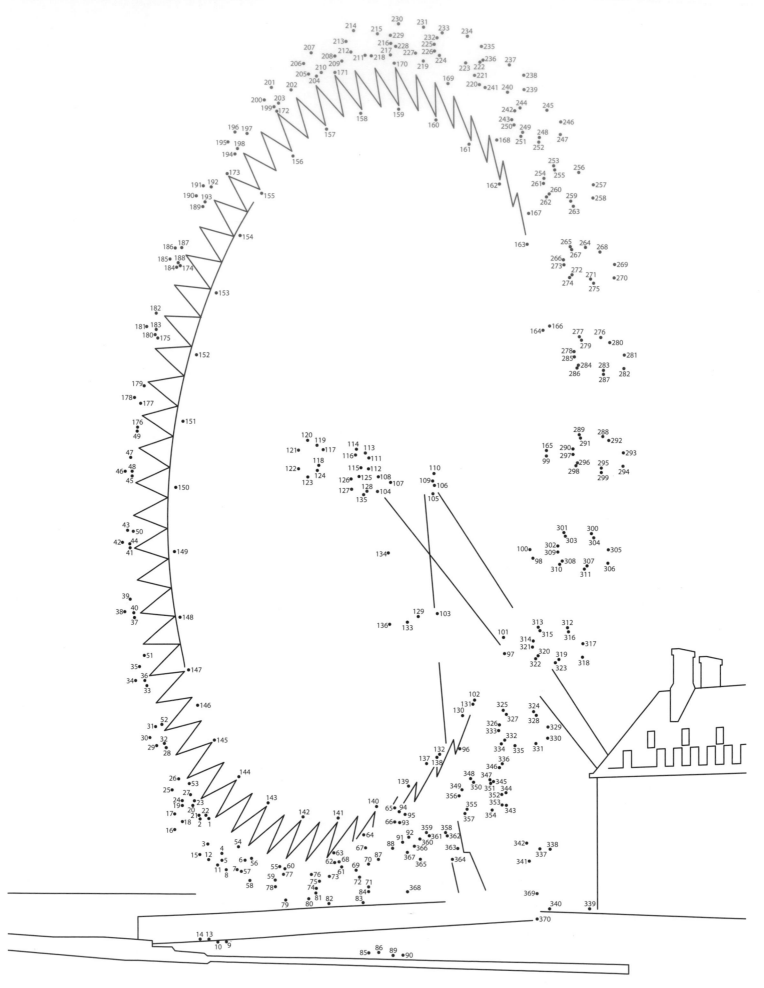

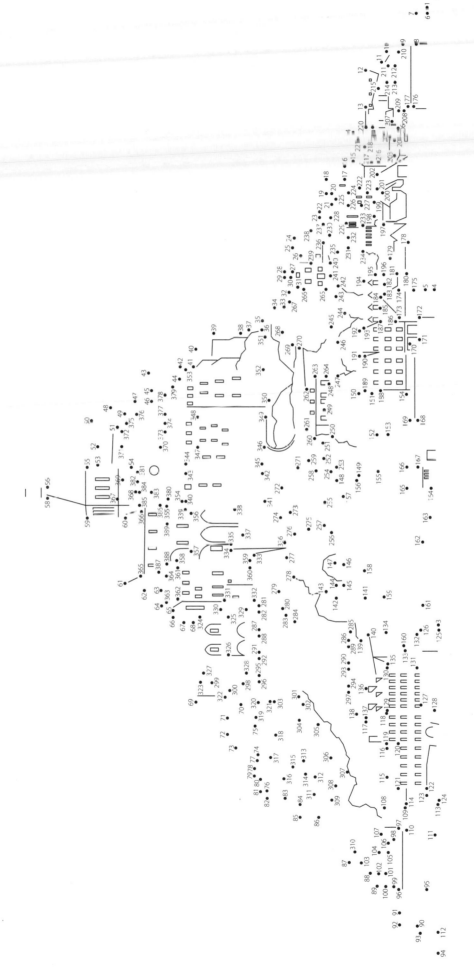

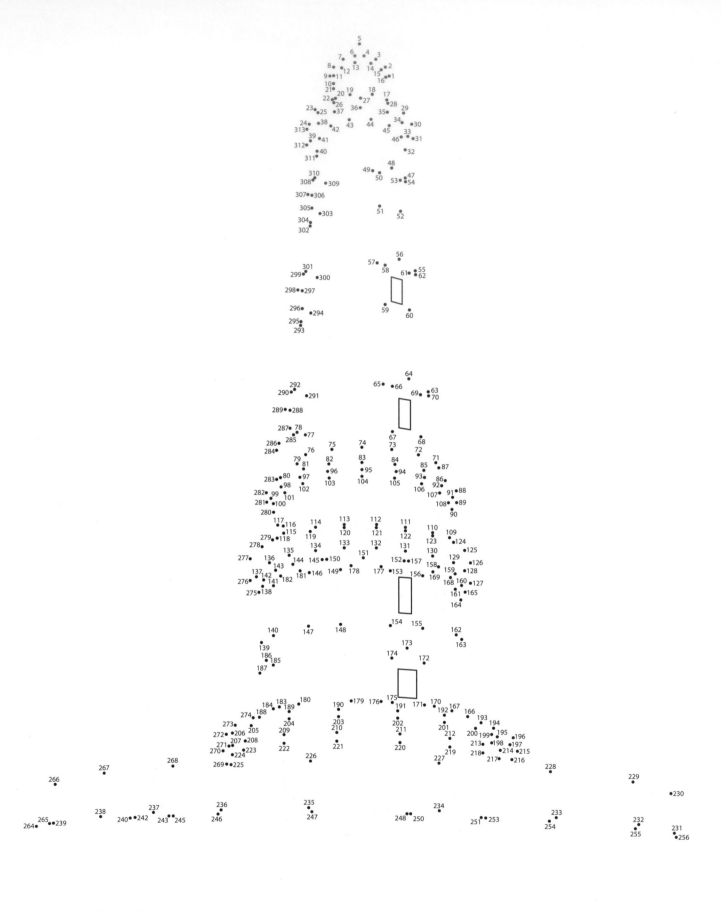

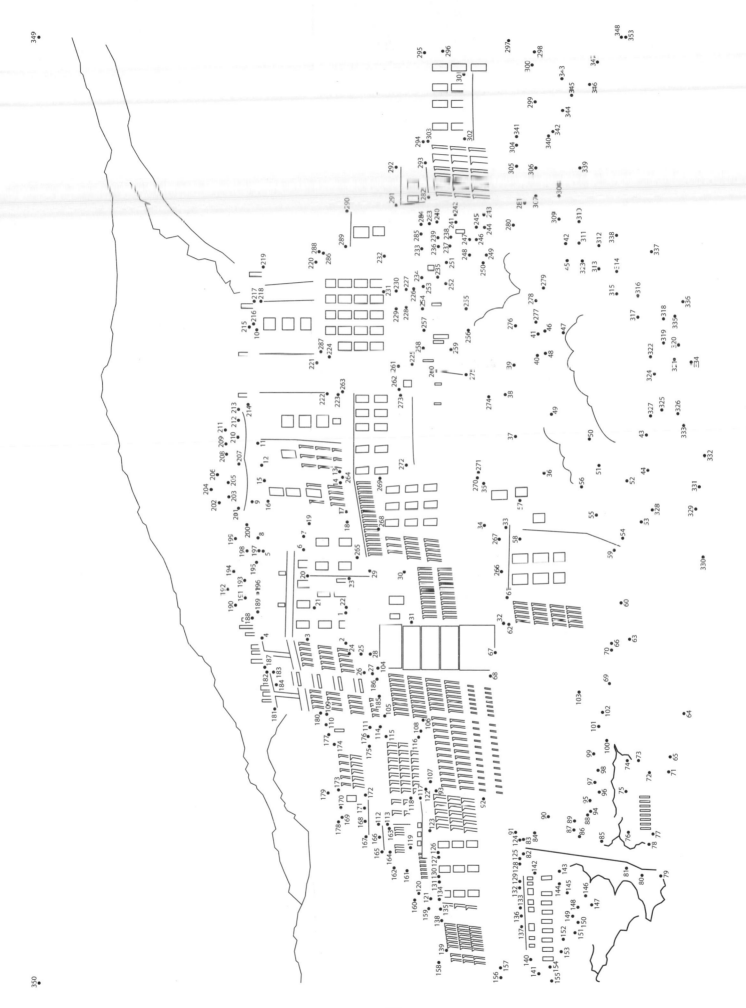

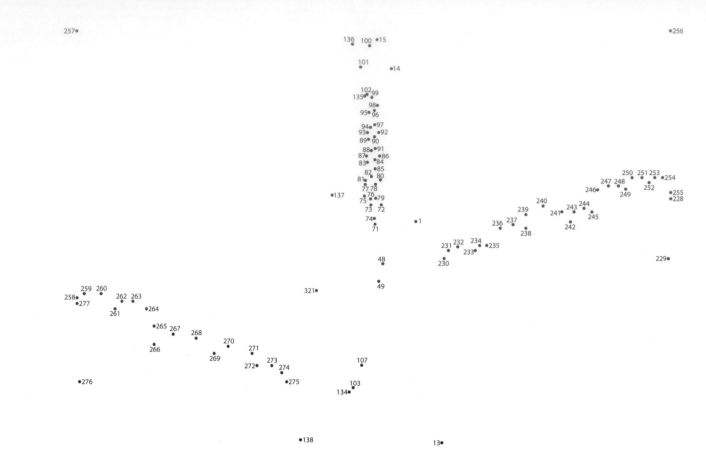

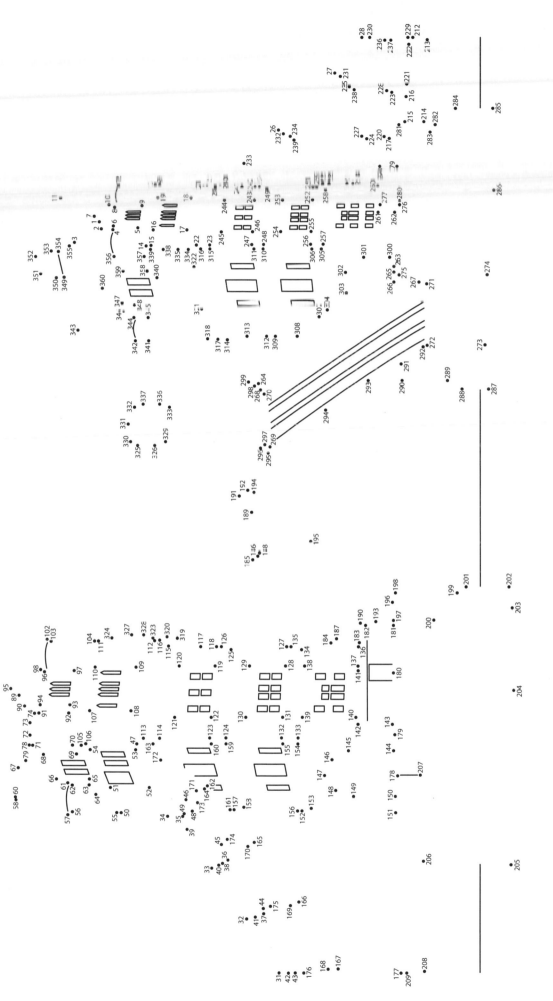

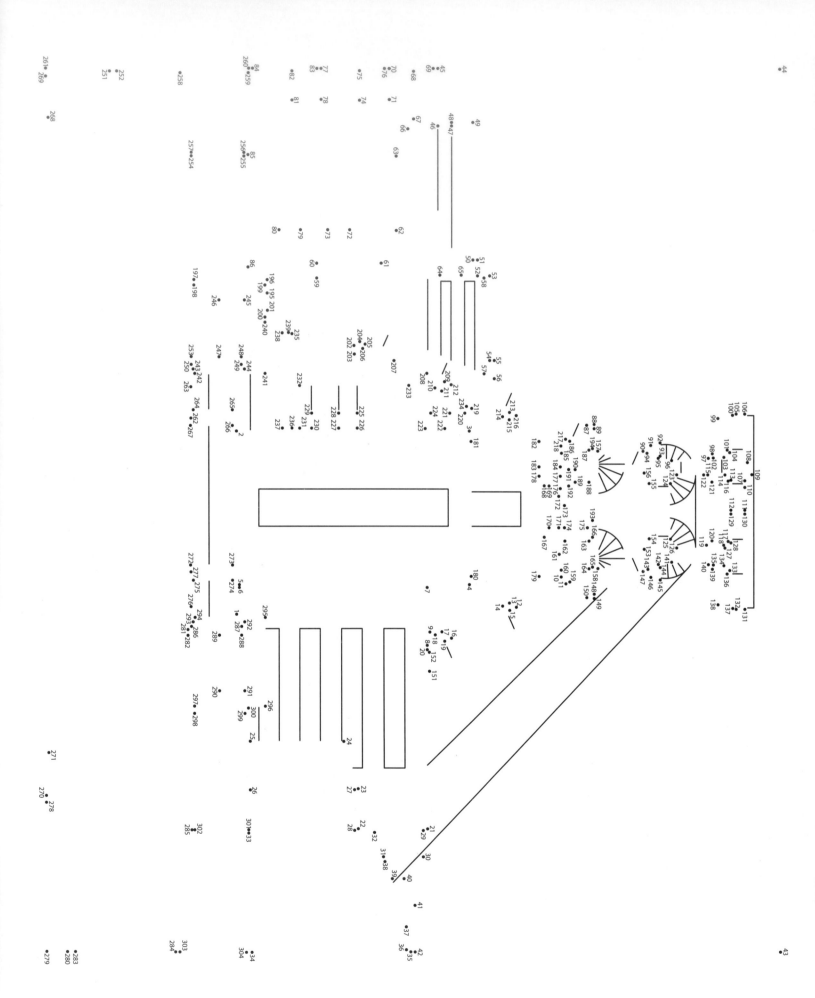

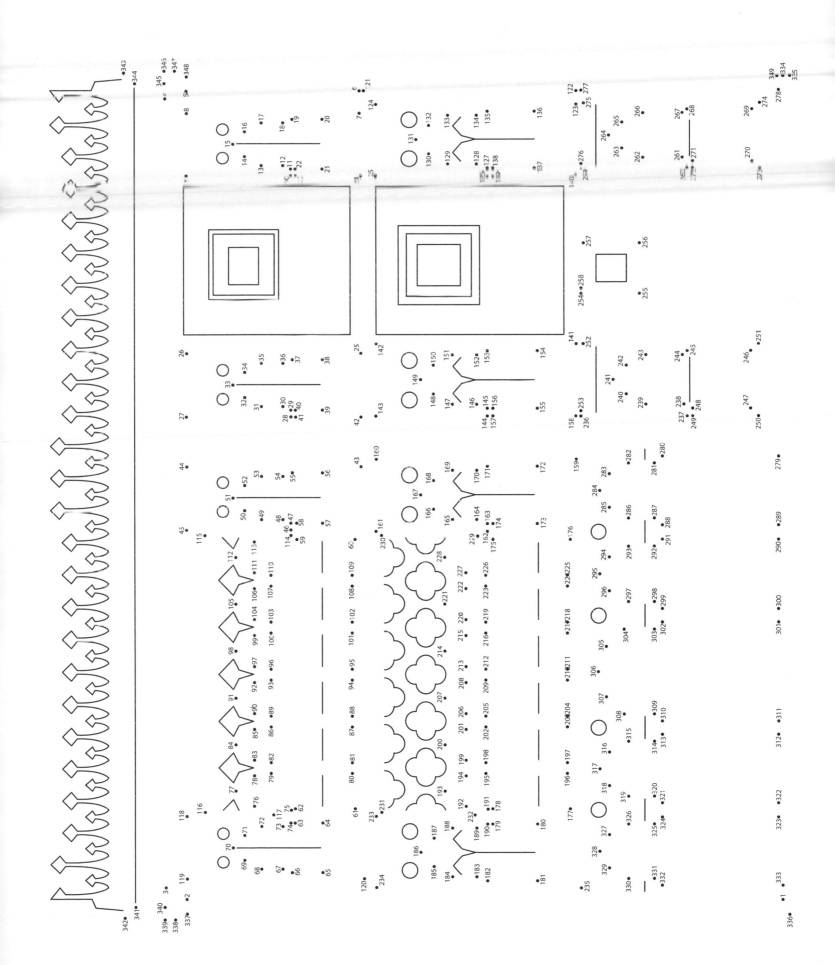

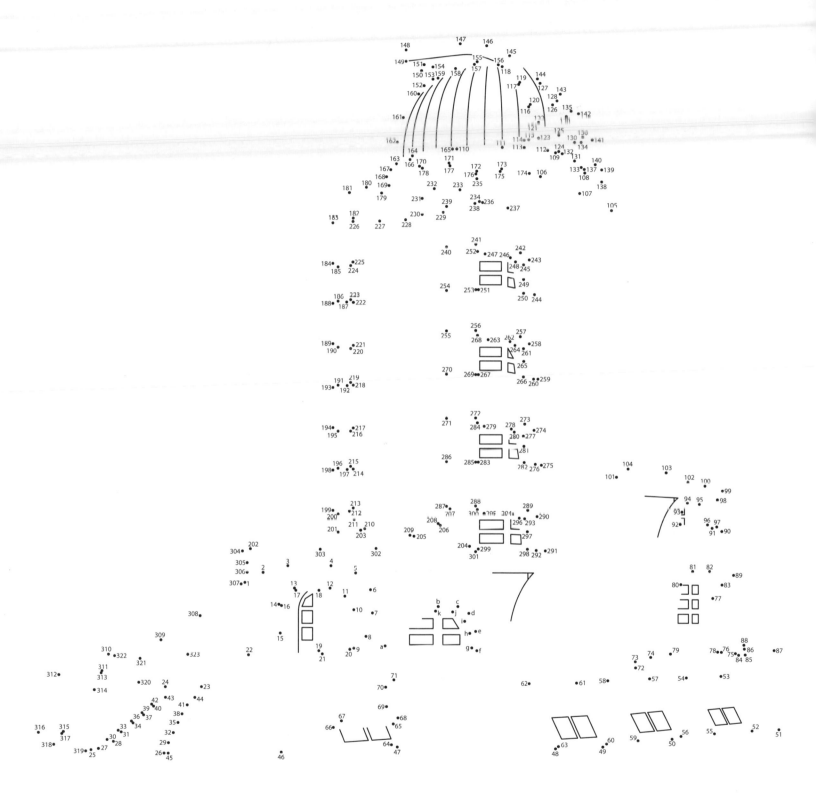

This picture is made from 2 continuous lines: a) numbers and b) lower case letters

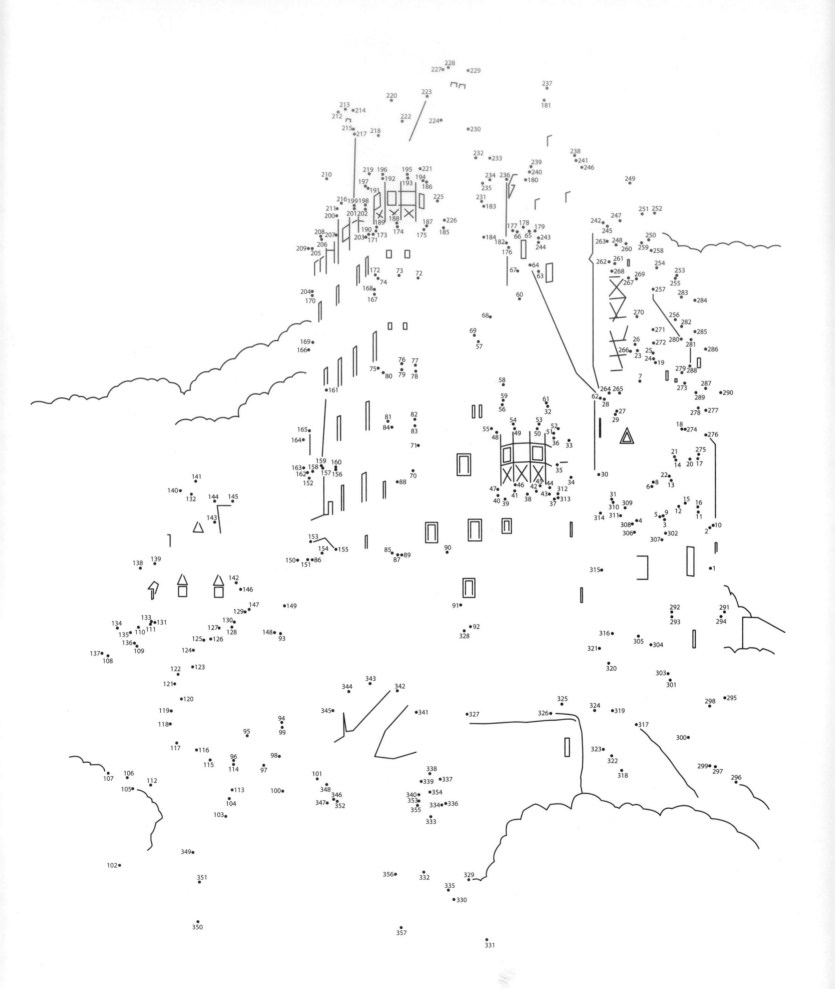

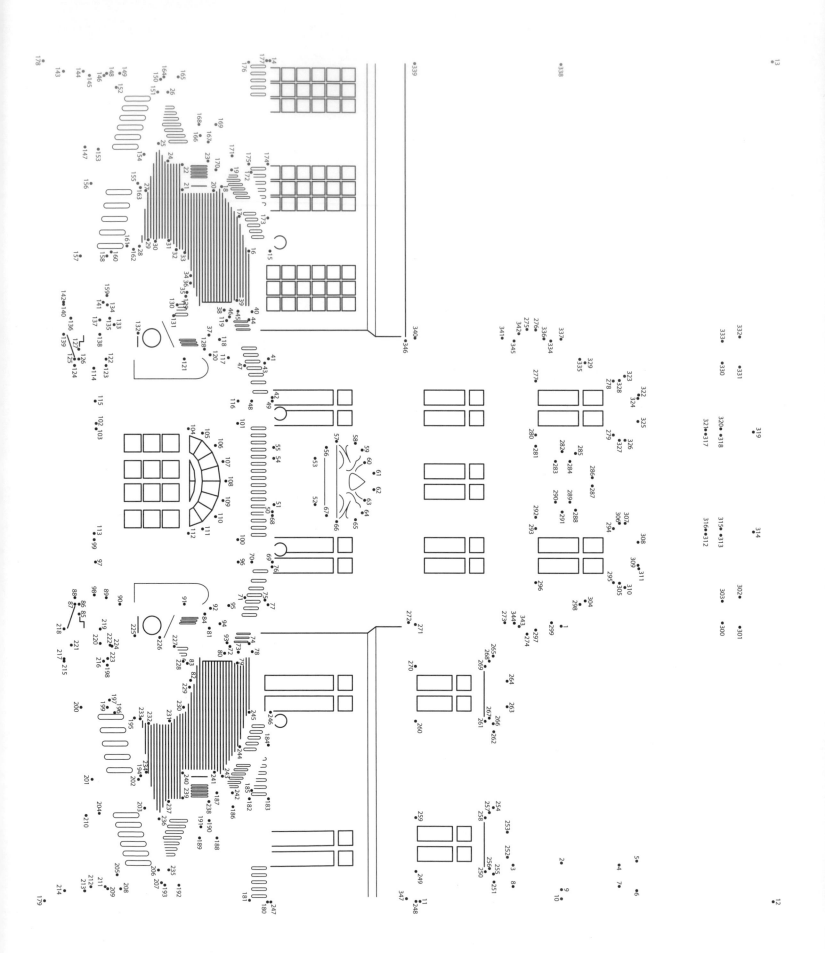

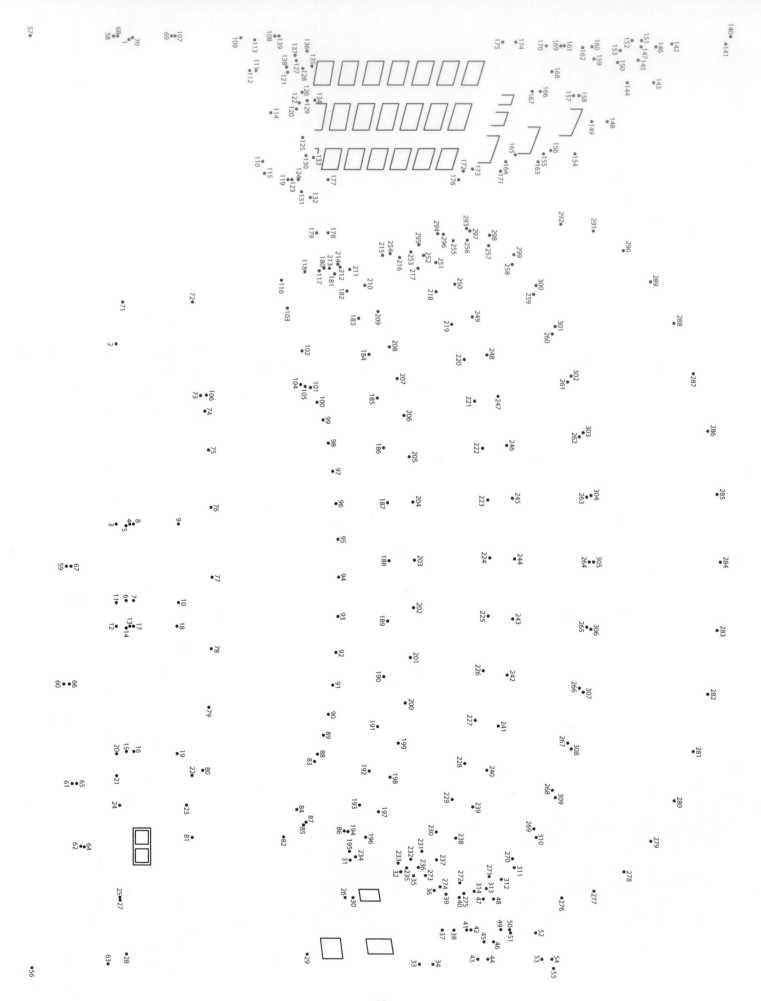

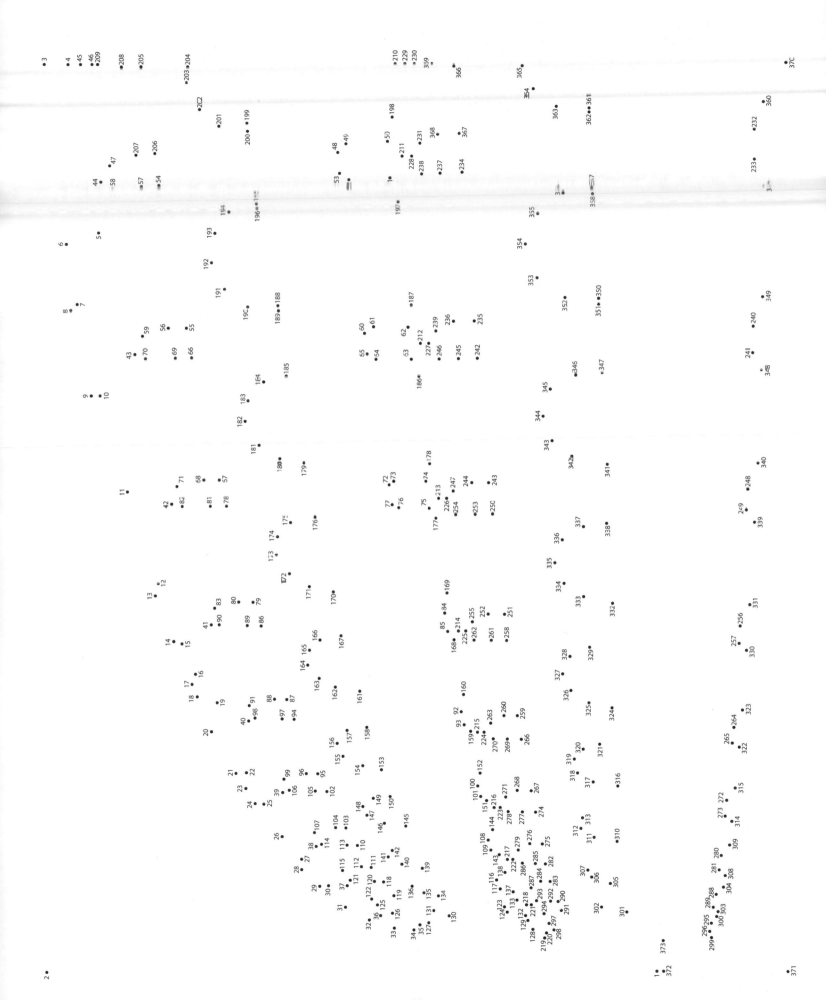

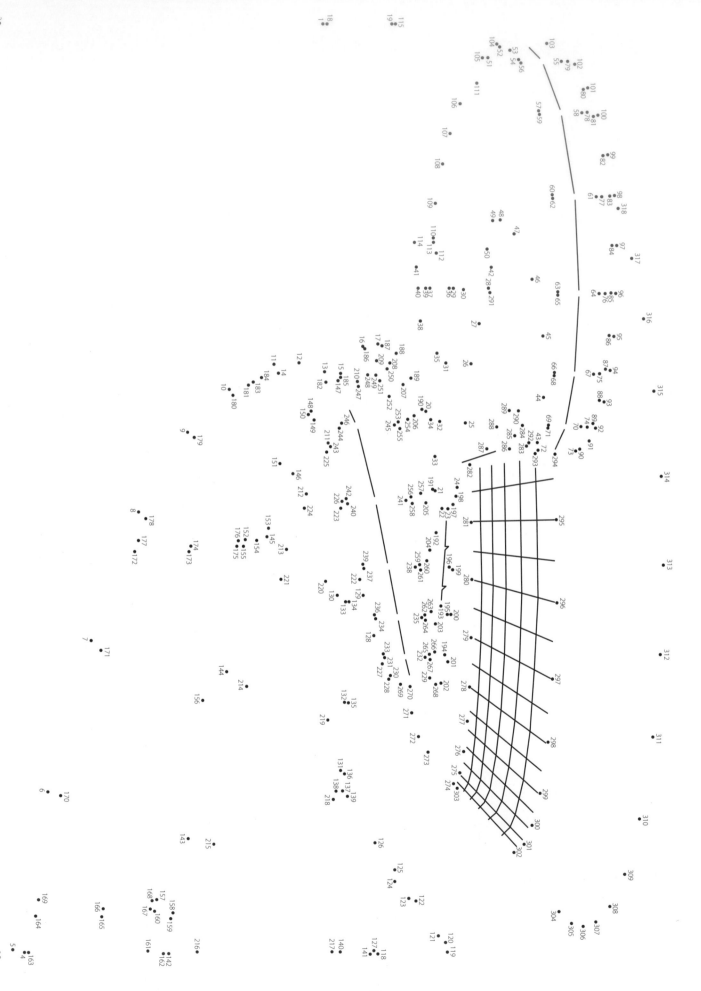

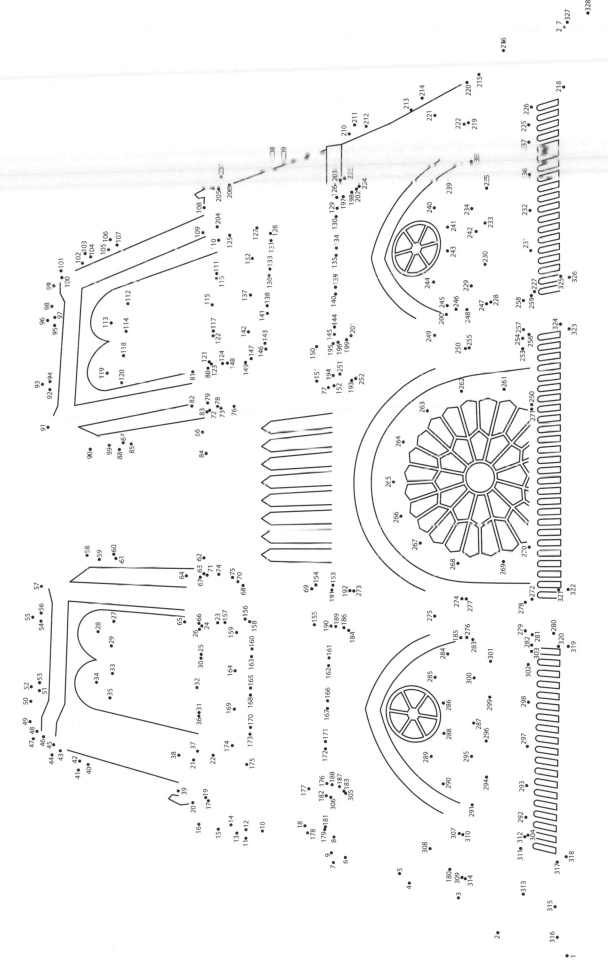

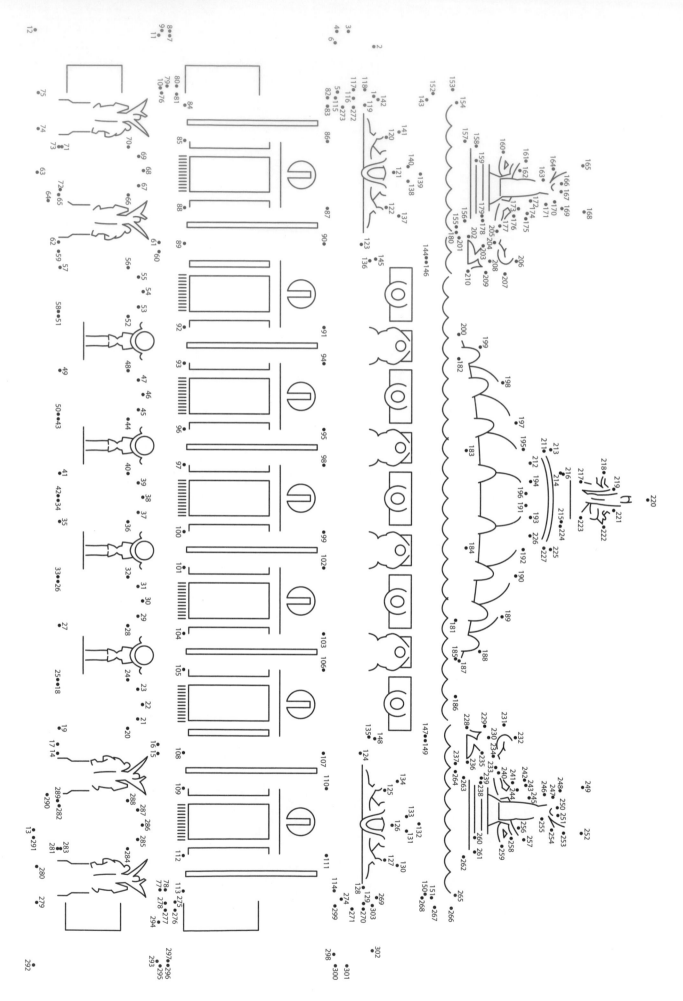

44

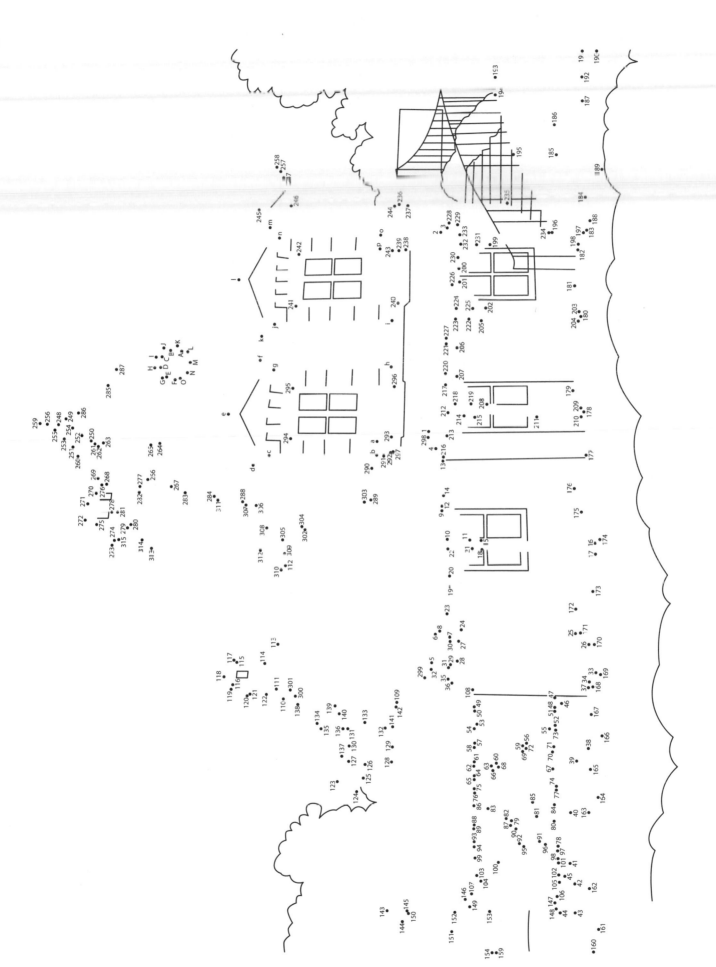

This picture is made from 3 continuous lines: a) numbers, b) upper case letters and c) lower case letters

45

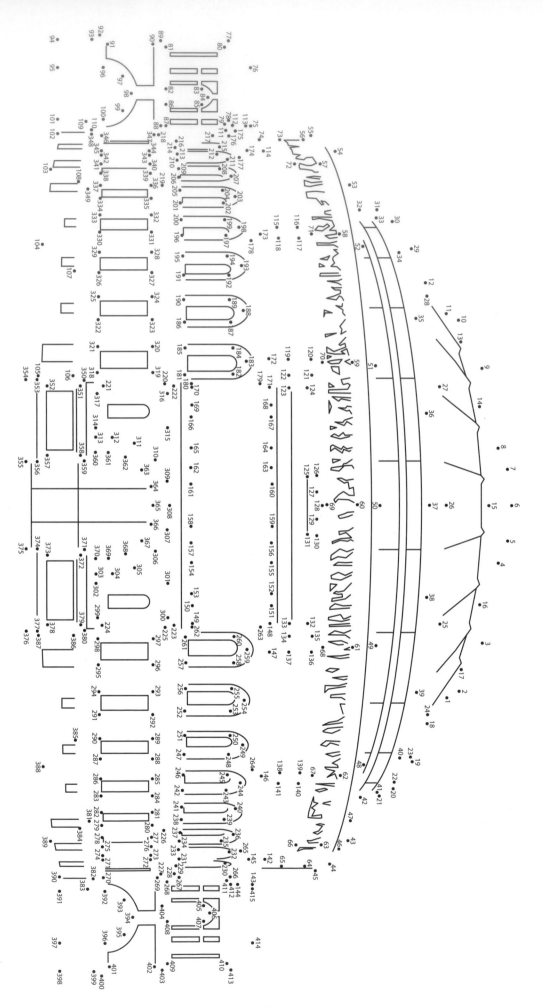

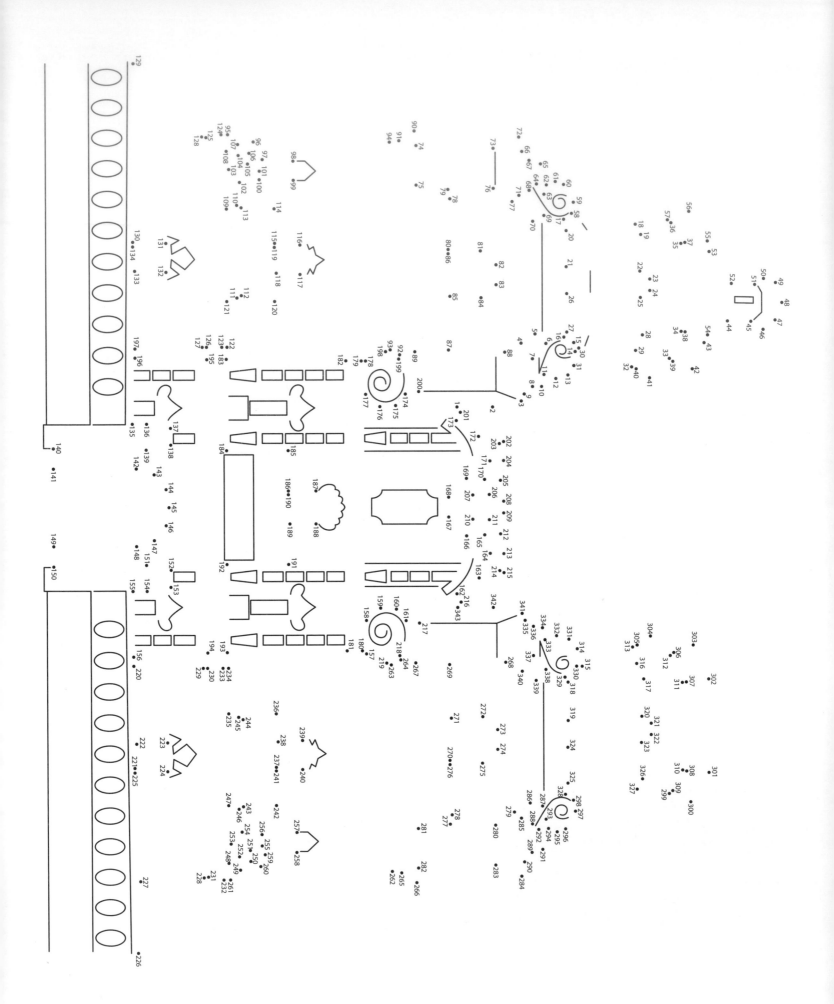

48

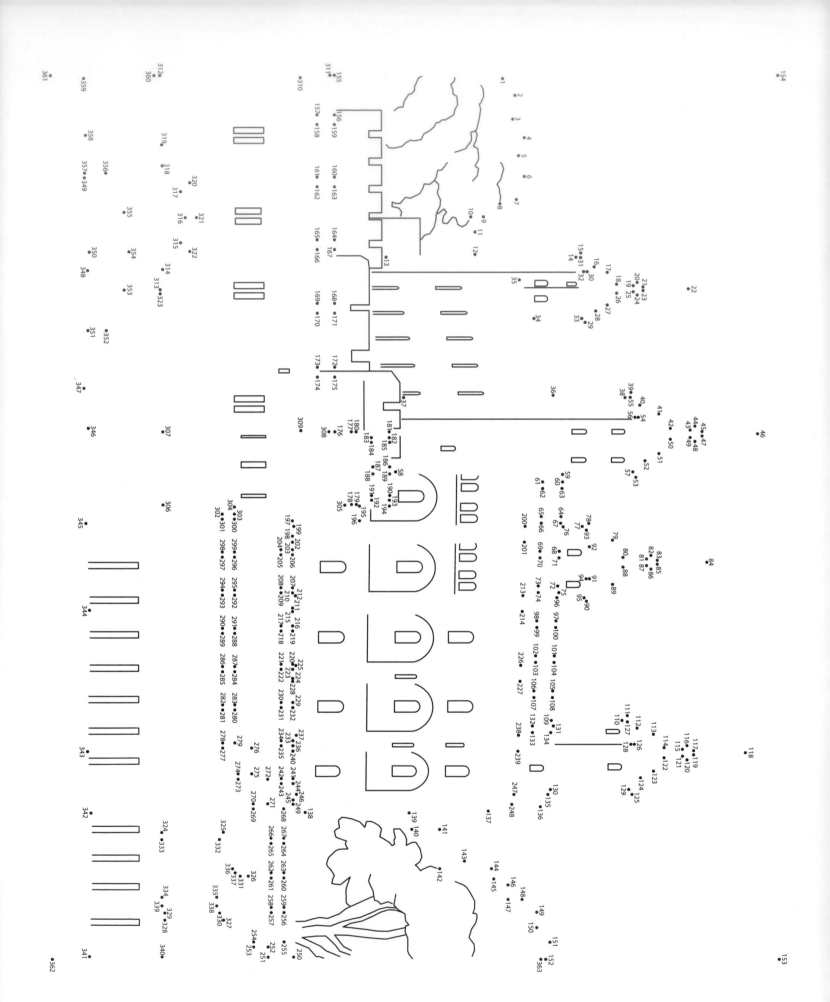

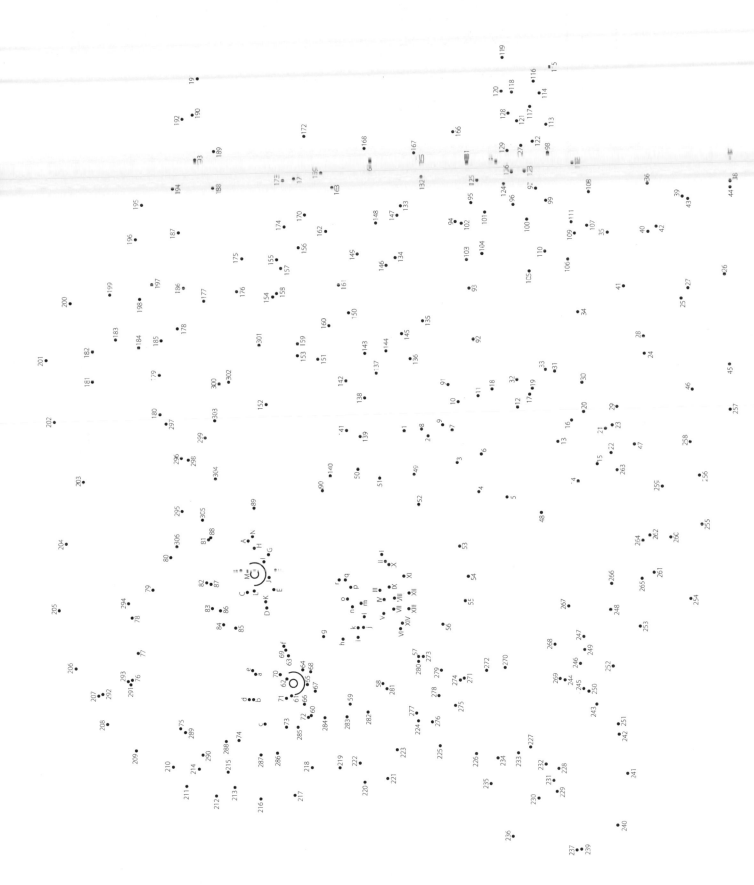

This picture is made from 4 continuous lines:
a) numbers, b) upper case letters, c) lower case letters and d) roman numerals

53

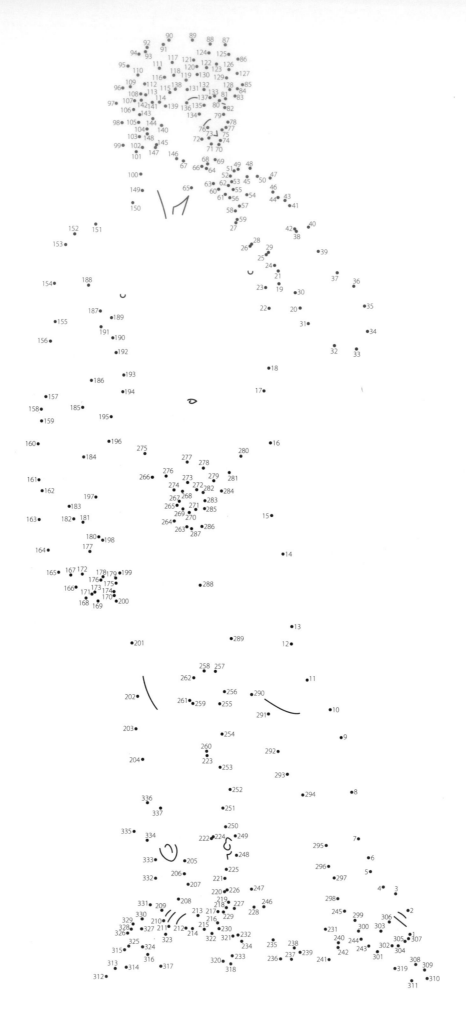

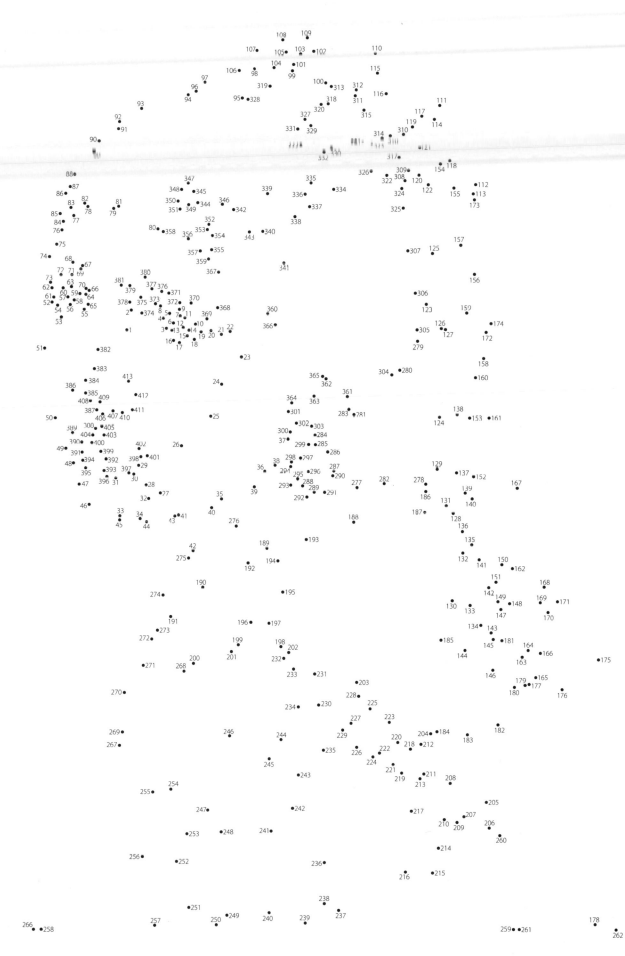

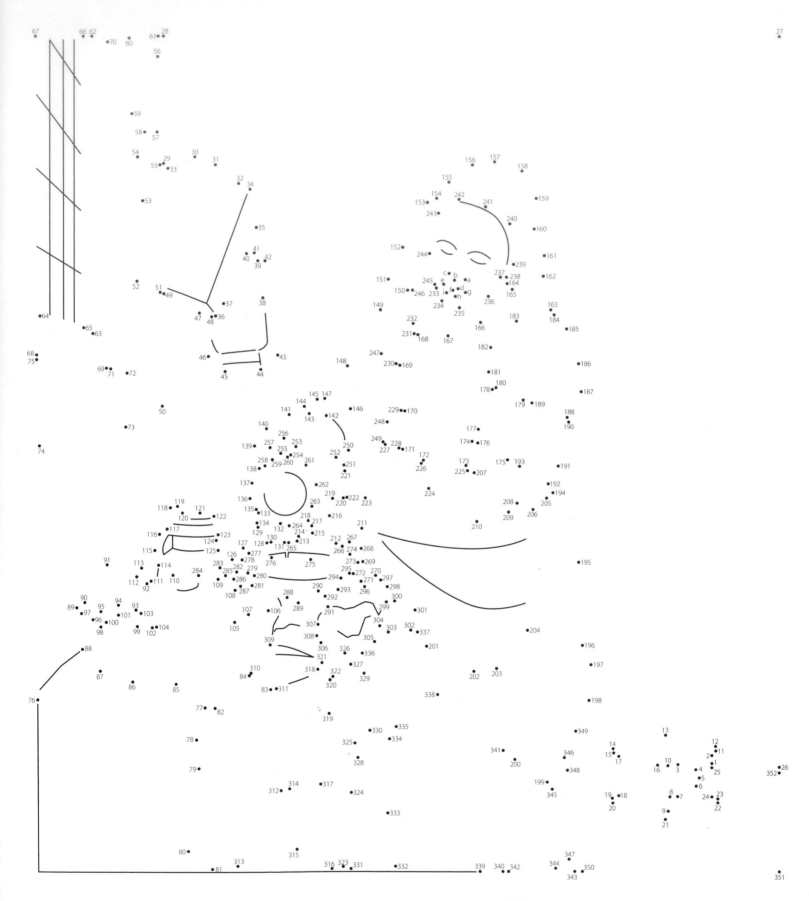

This picture is made from 2 continuous lines: a) numbers and b) lower case letters

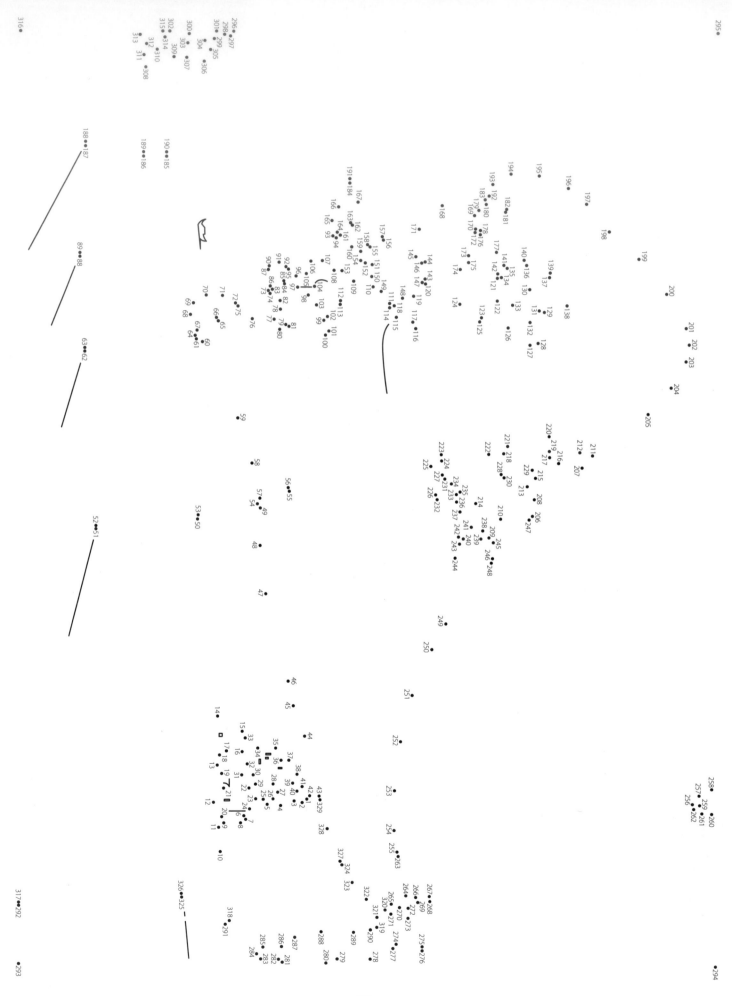

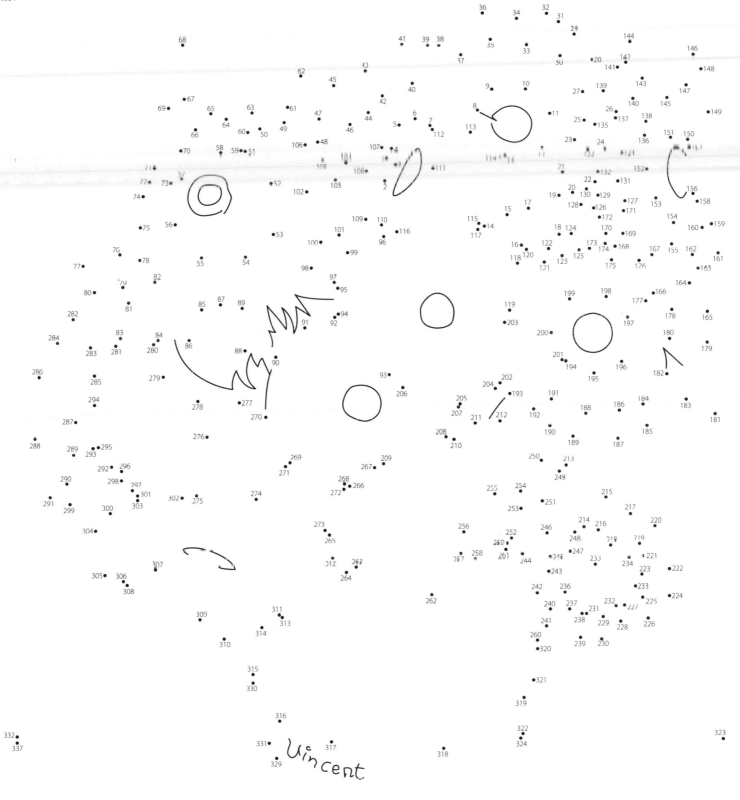

Vincent

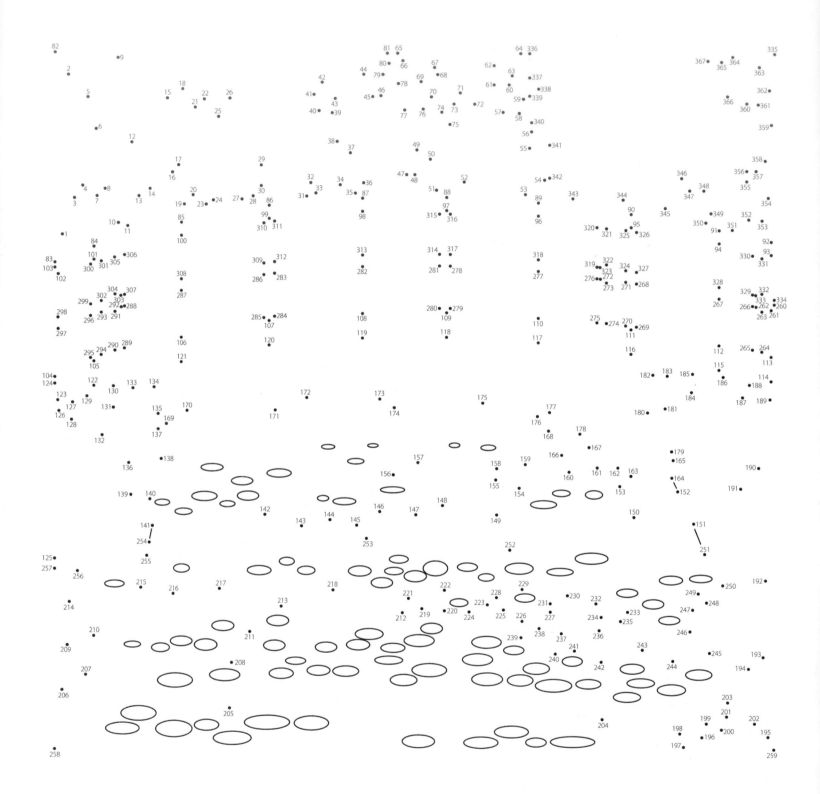

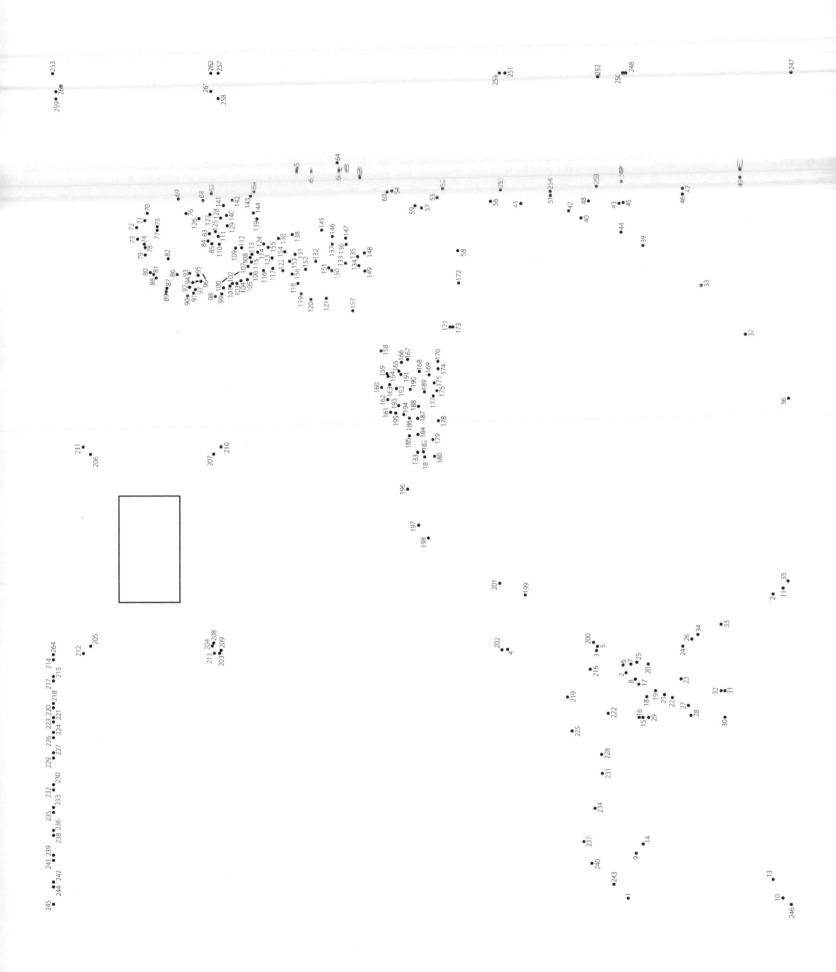

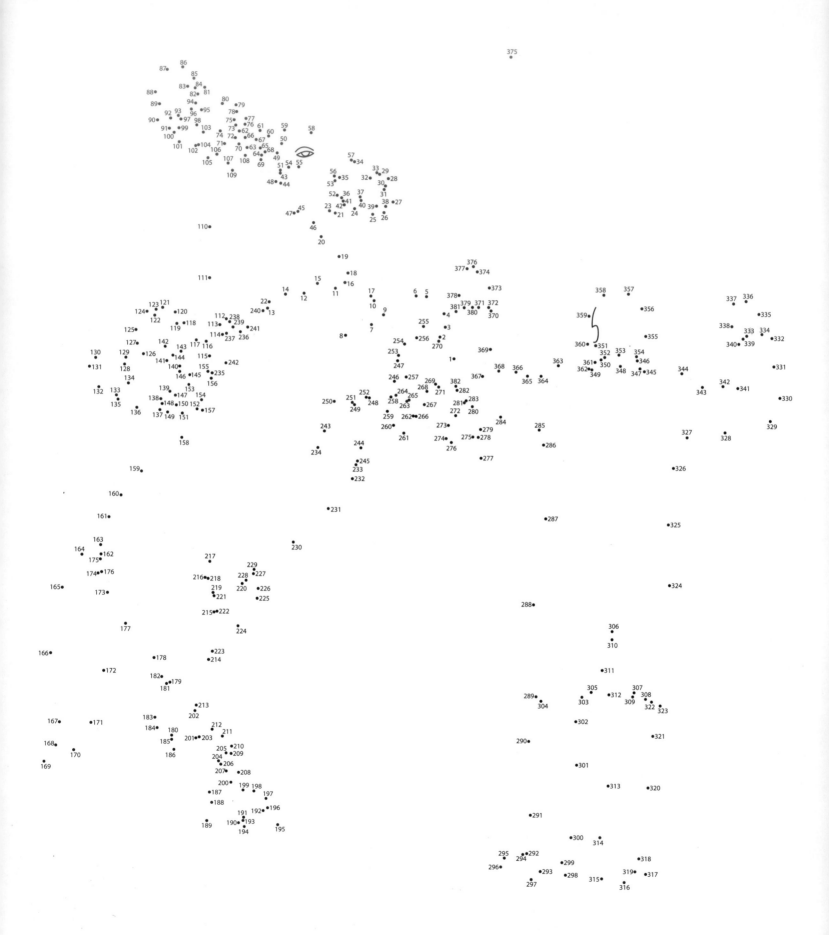

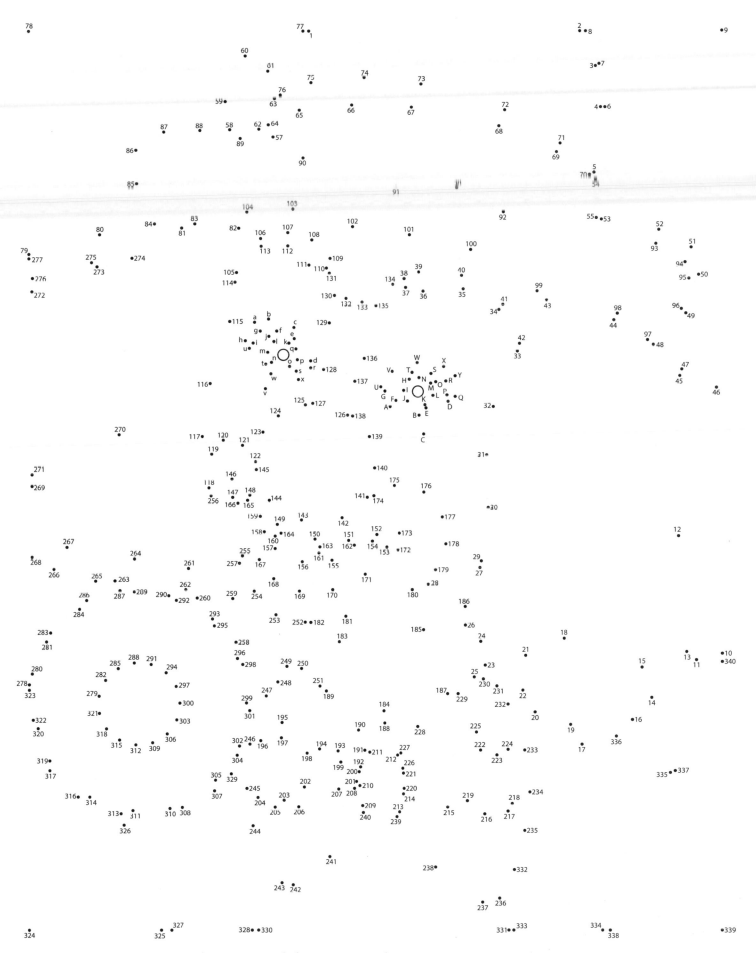

This picture is made from 3 continuous lines:
a) numbers, b) upper case letters and c) lower case letters

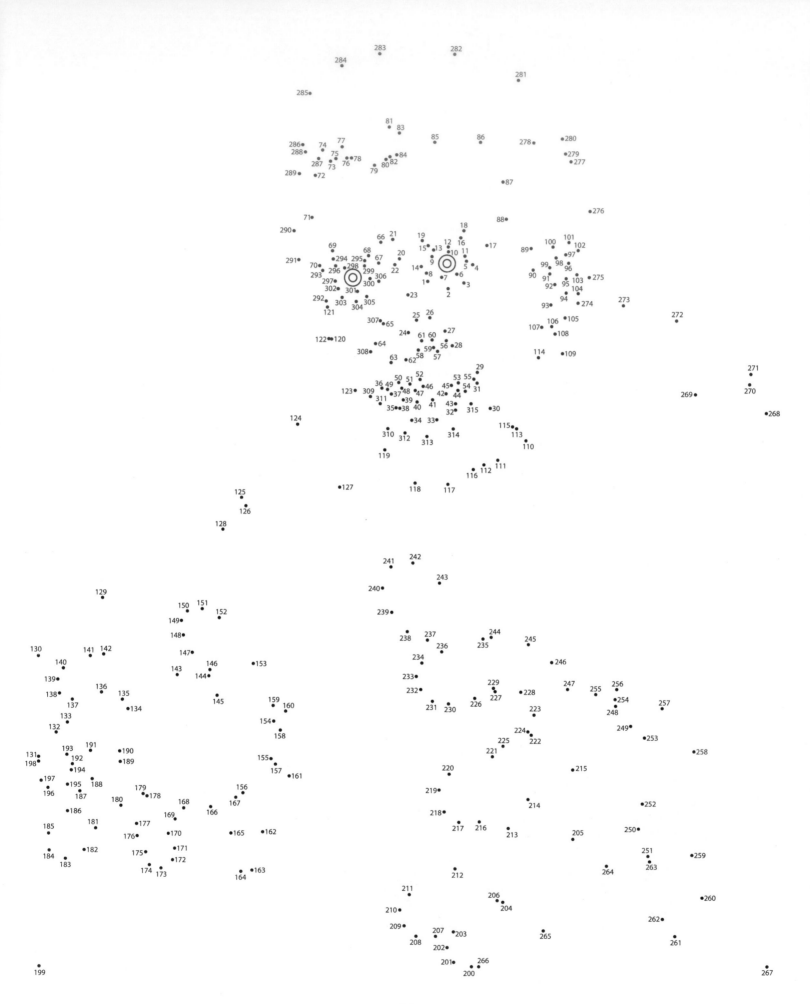

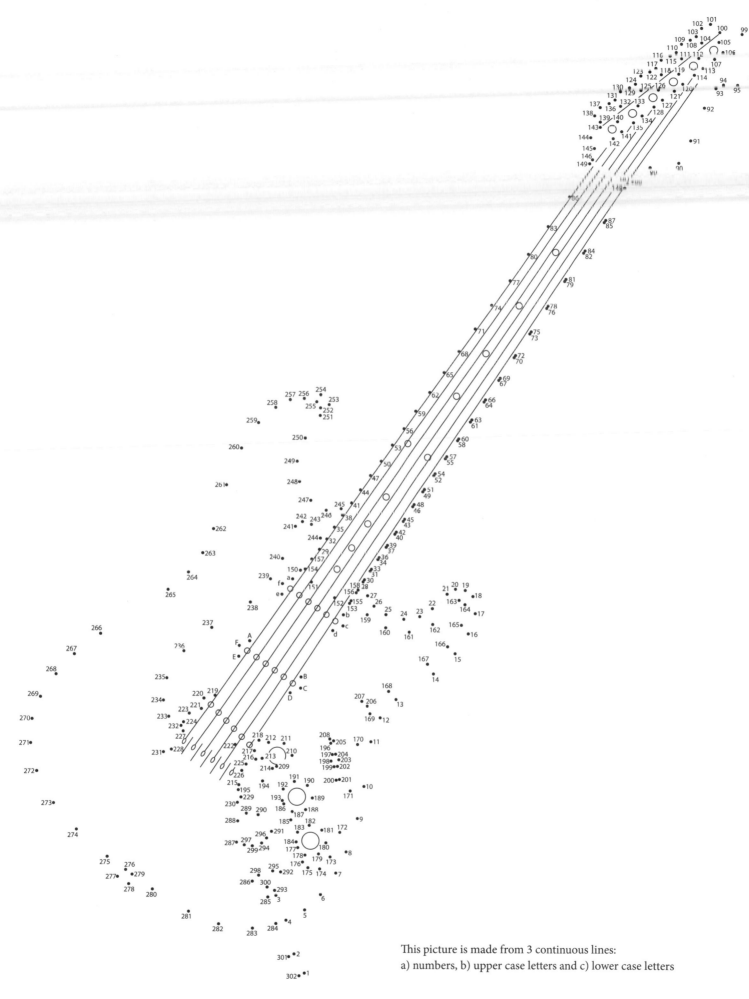

This picture is made from 3 continuous lines:
a) numbers, b) upper case letters and c) lower case letters

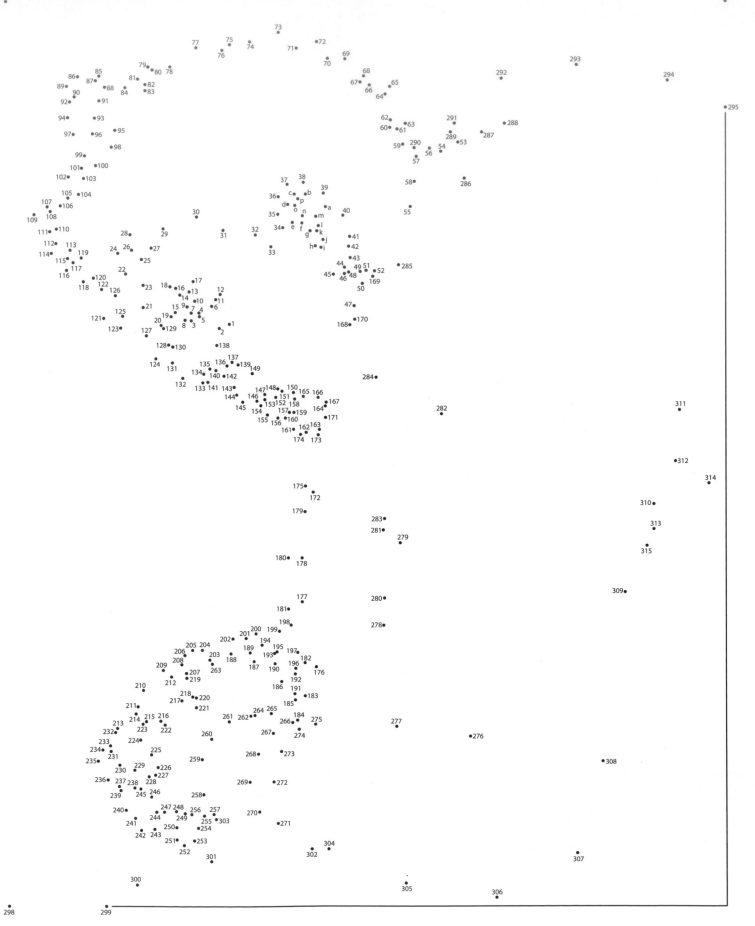

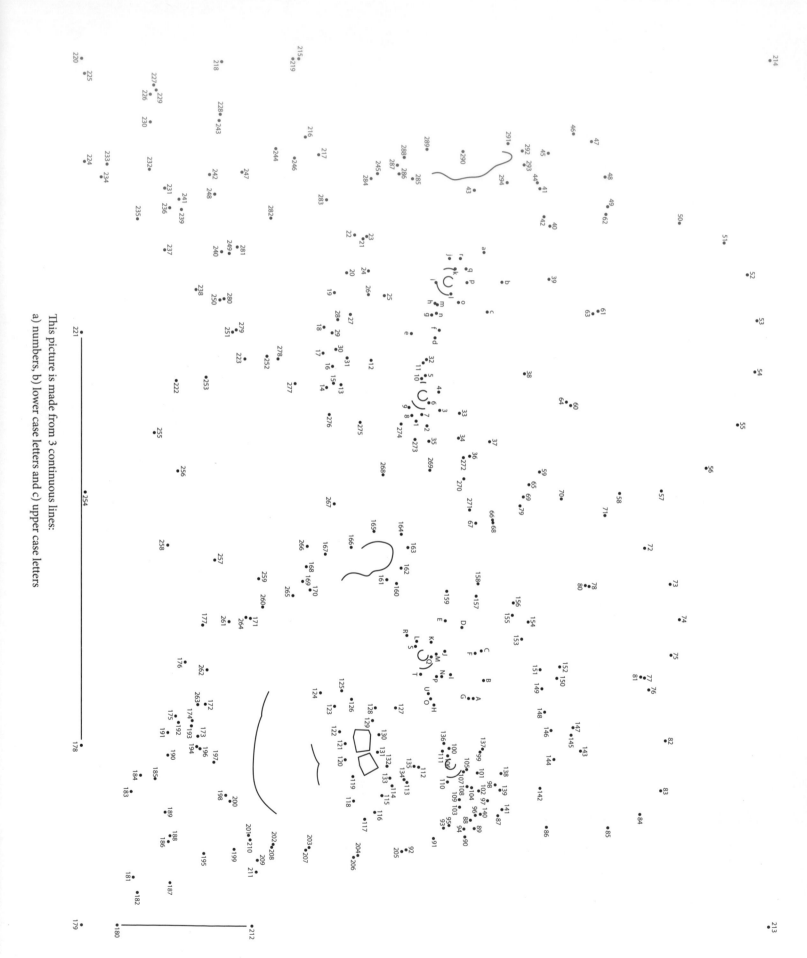

This picture is made from 3 continuous lines:
a) numbers, b) lower case letters and c) upper case letters

70

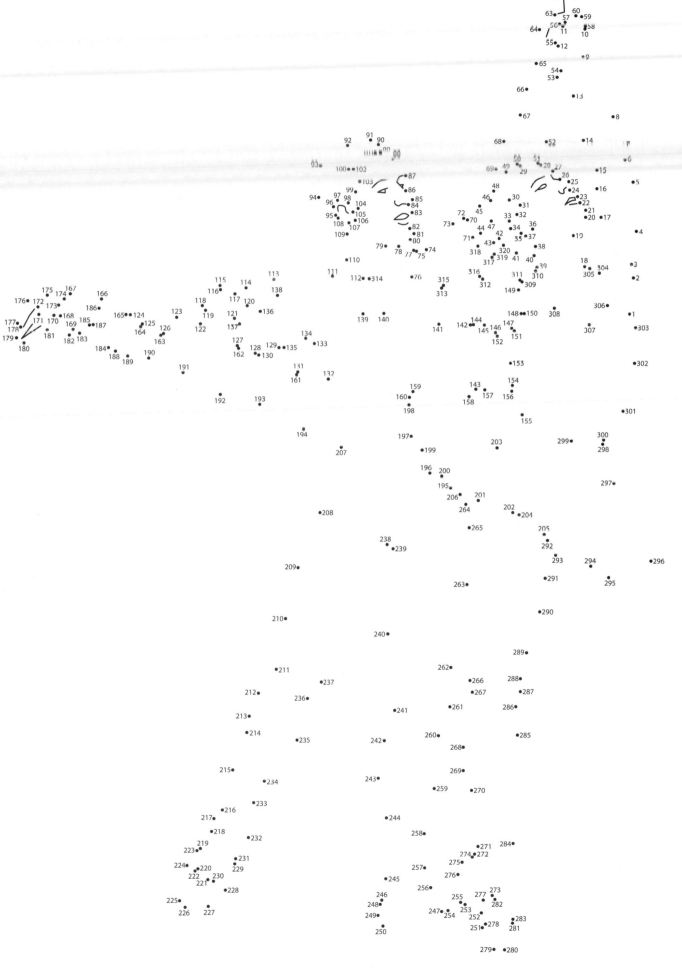

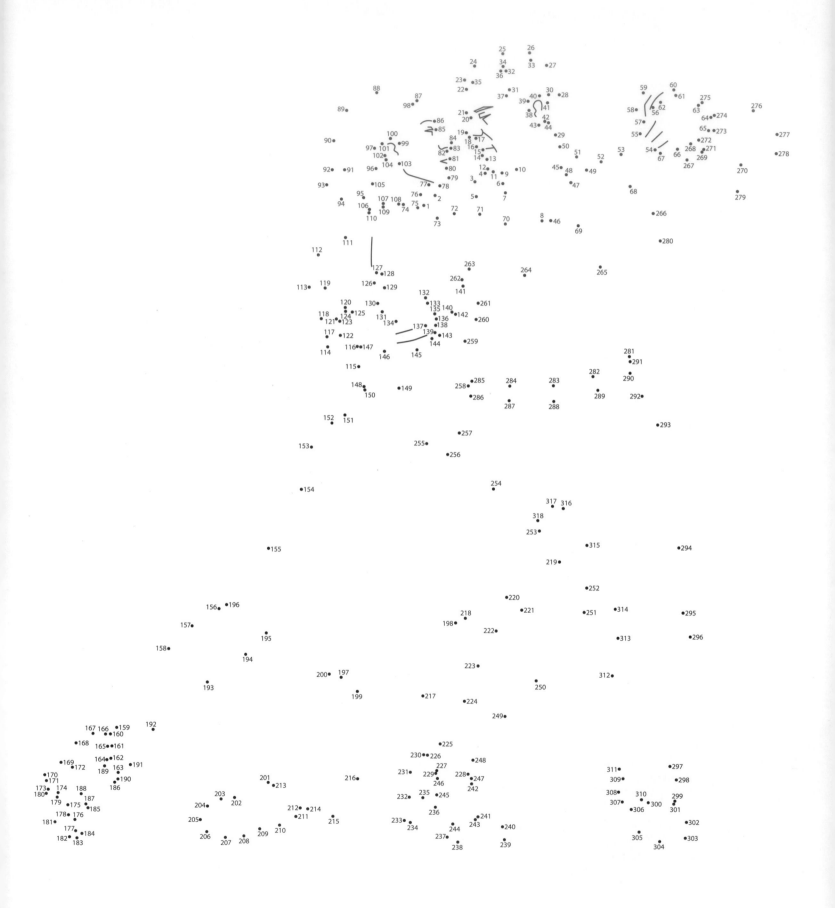

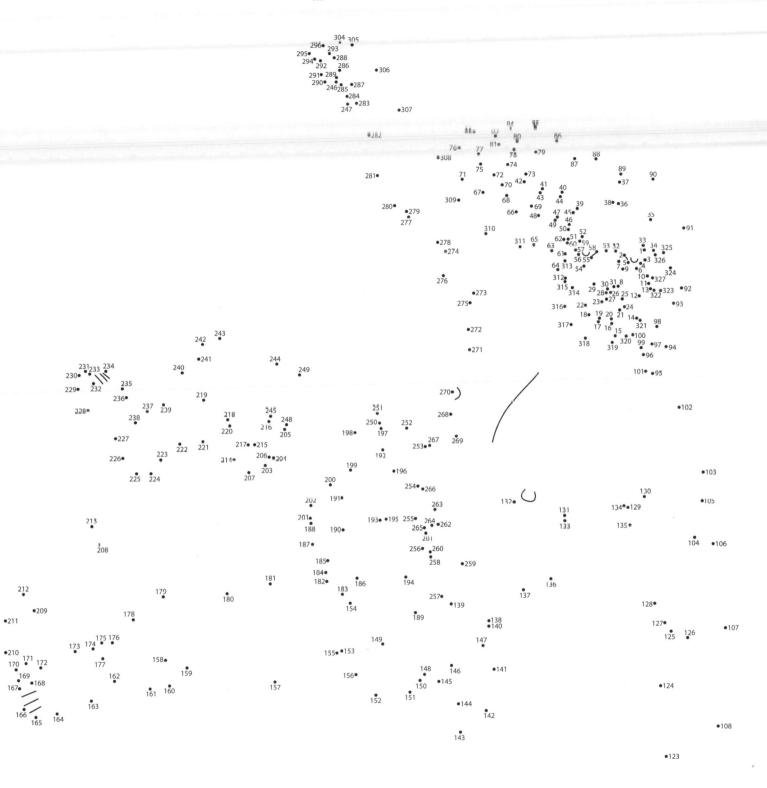

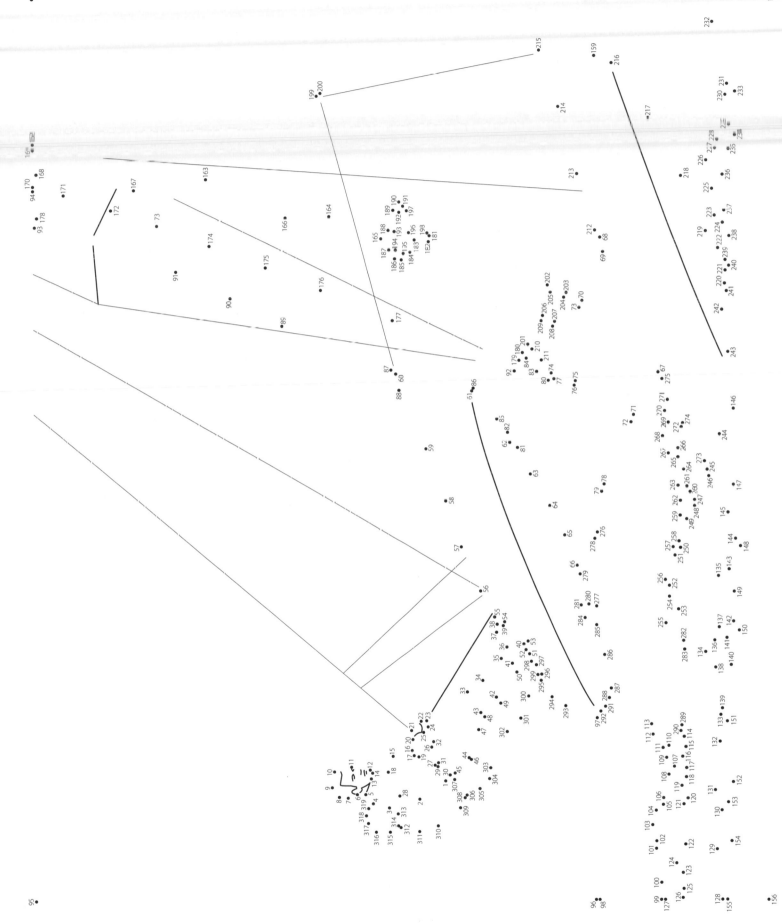

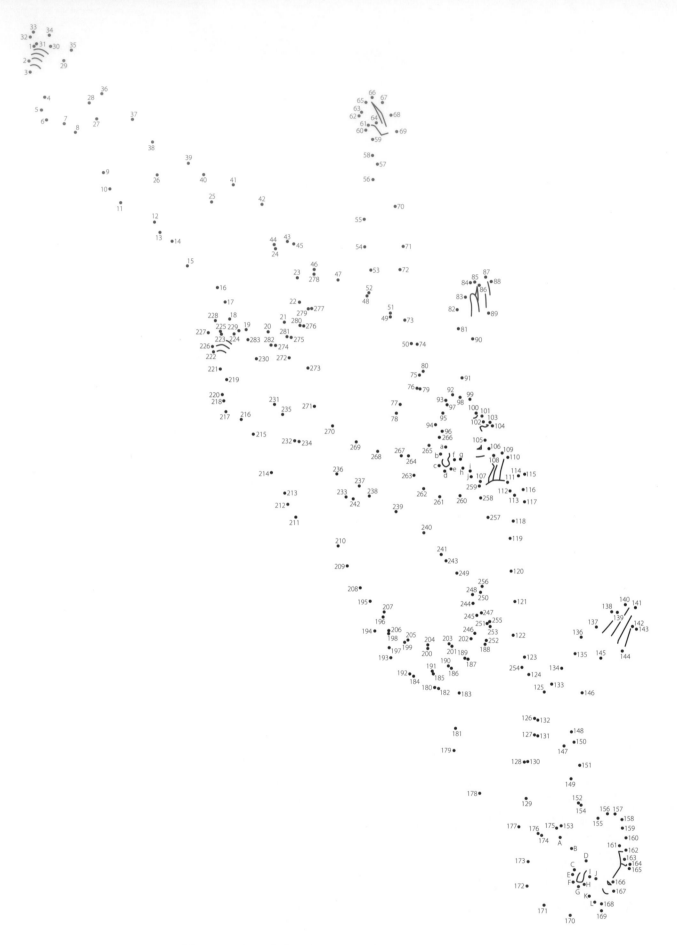

This picture is made from 3 continuous lines:
a) numbers, b) lower case letters and c) upper case letters

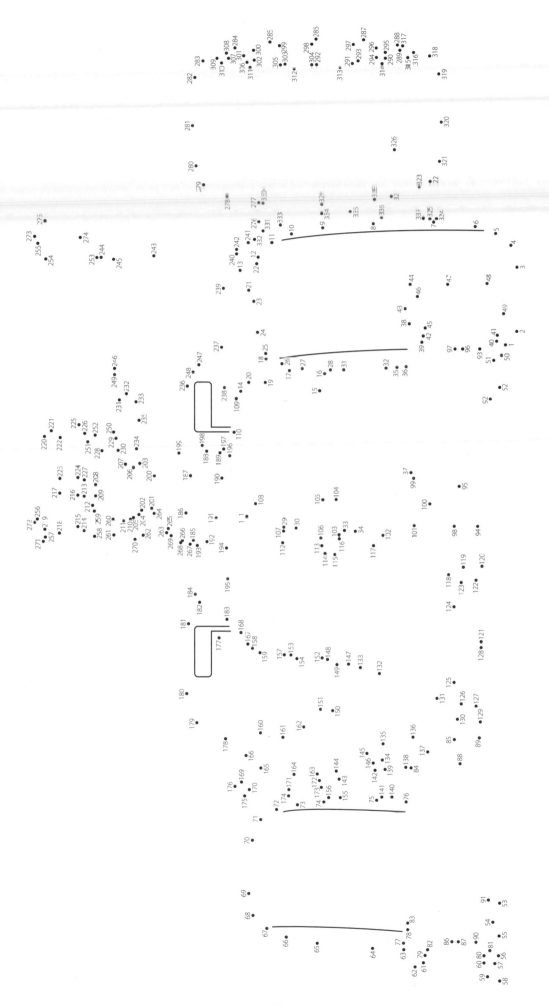

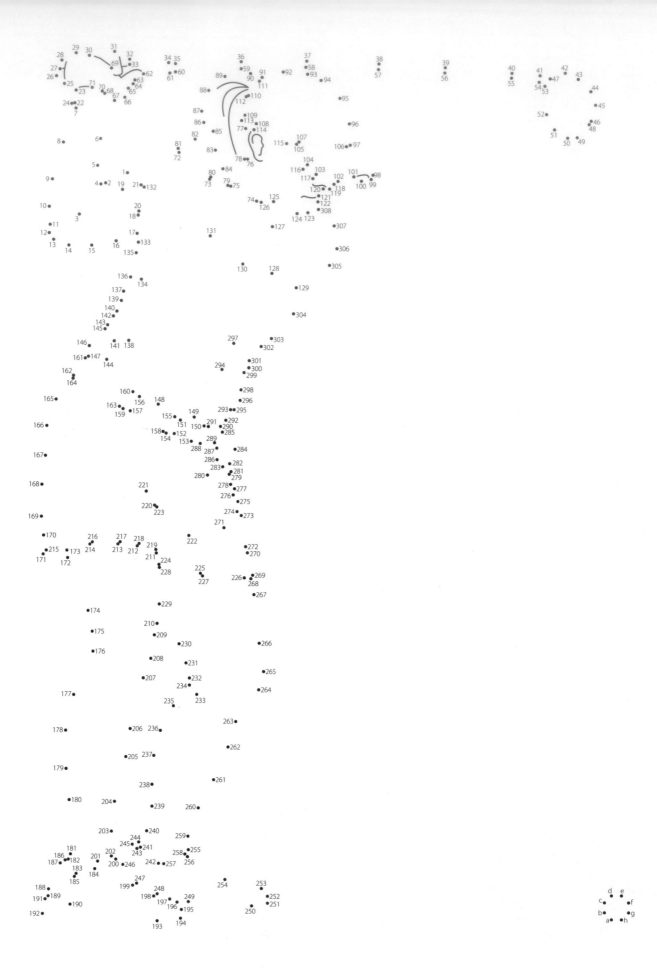

This picture is made from 2 continuous lines: a) numbers and b) lower case letters

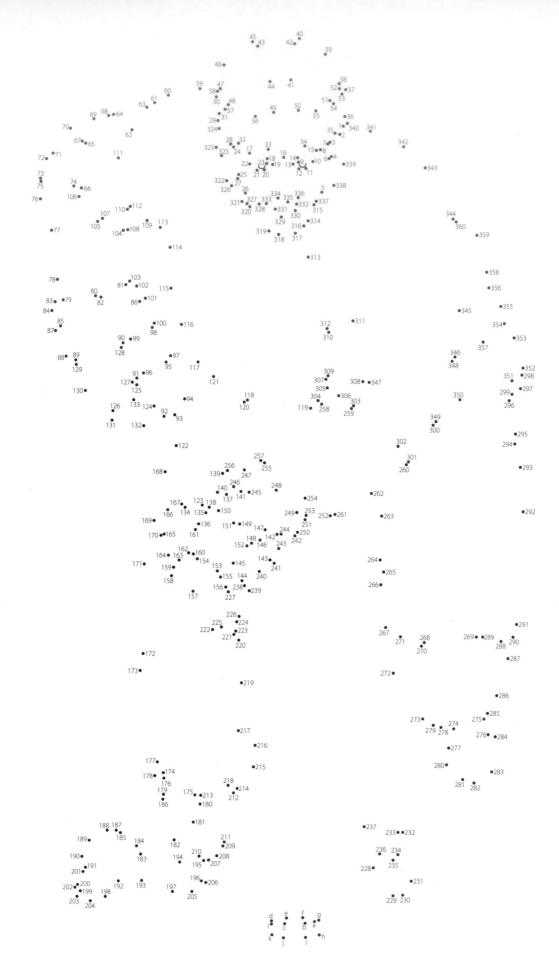

This picture is made from 2 continuous lines: a) numbers and b) lower case letters

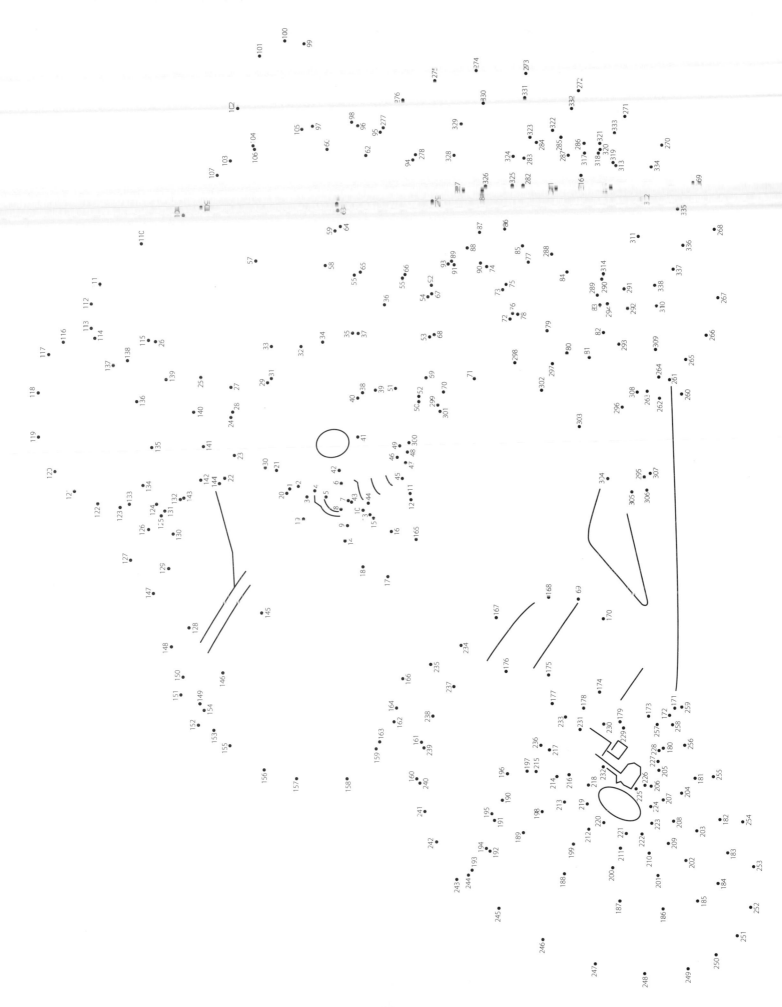

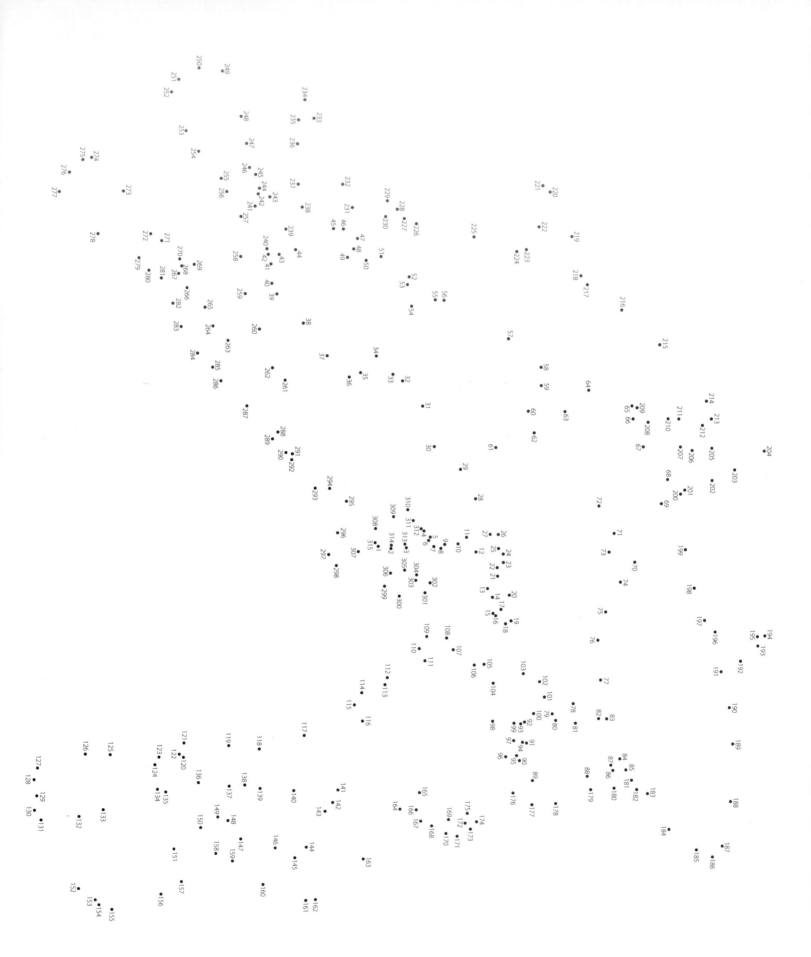

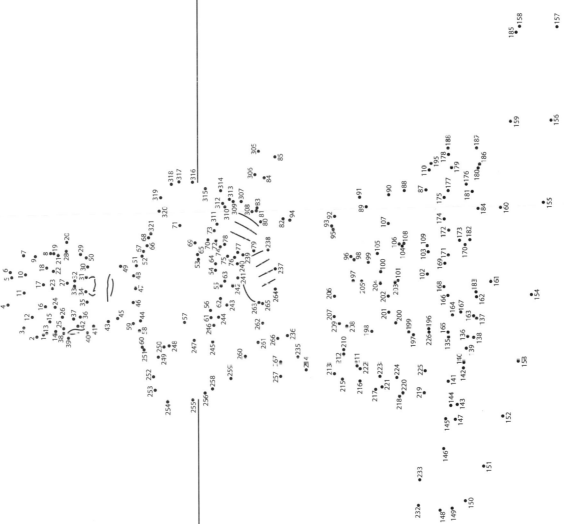

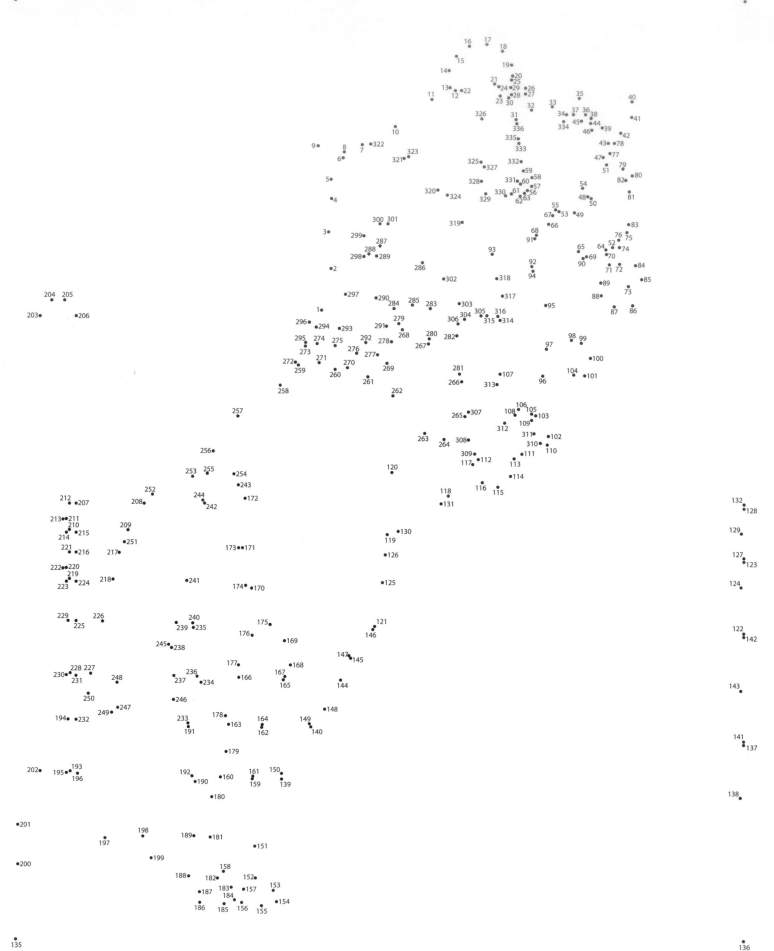

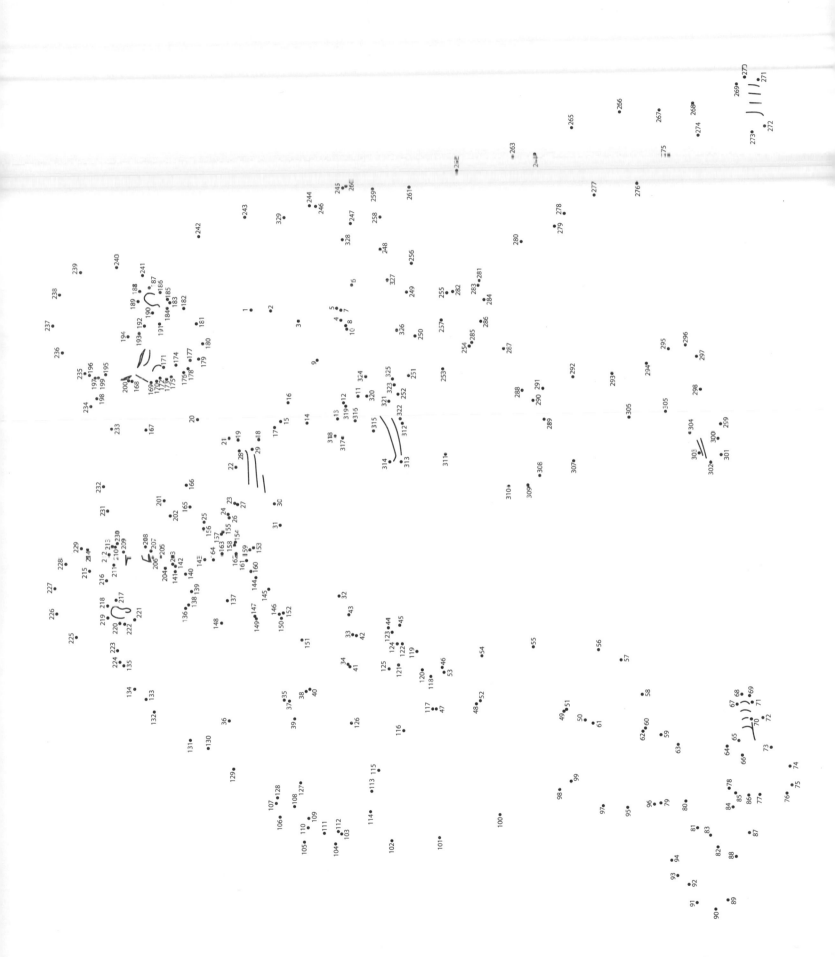

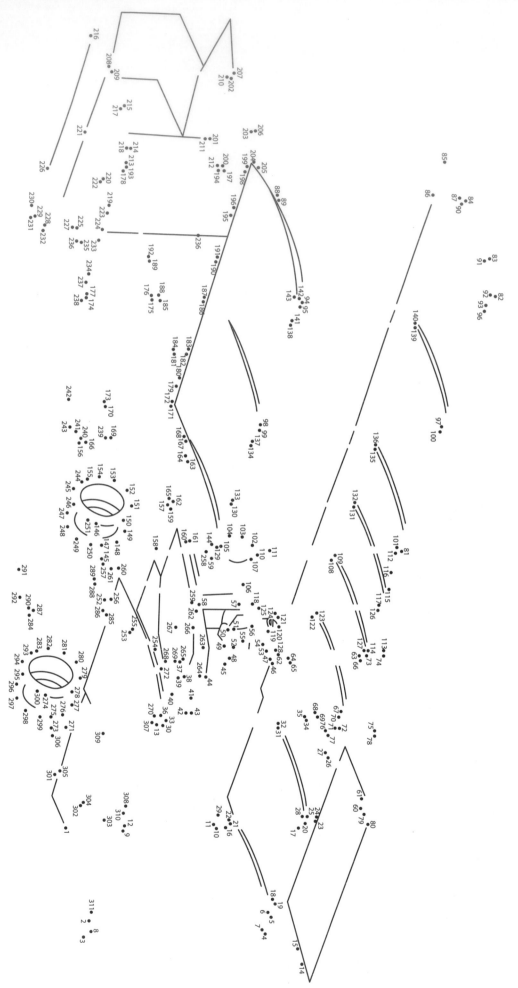

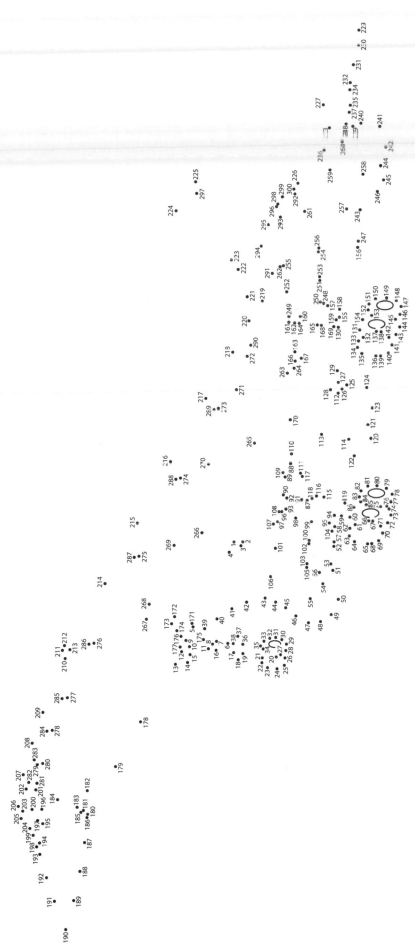

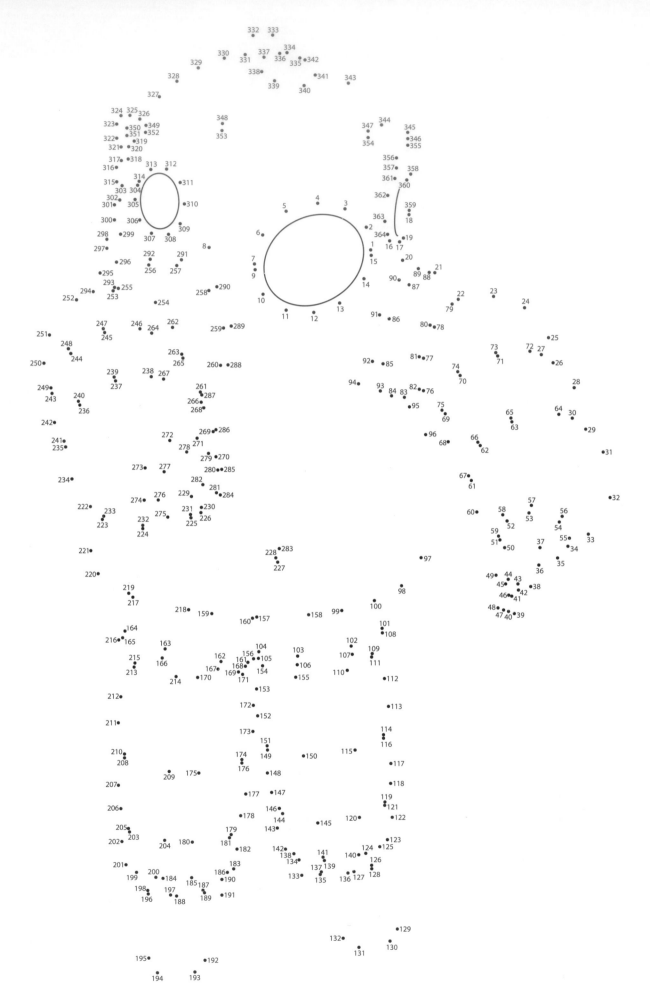

This picture is made from 2 continuous lines: a) numbers and b) lower case letters

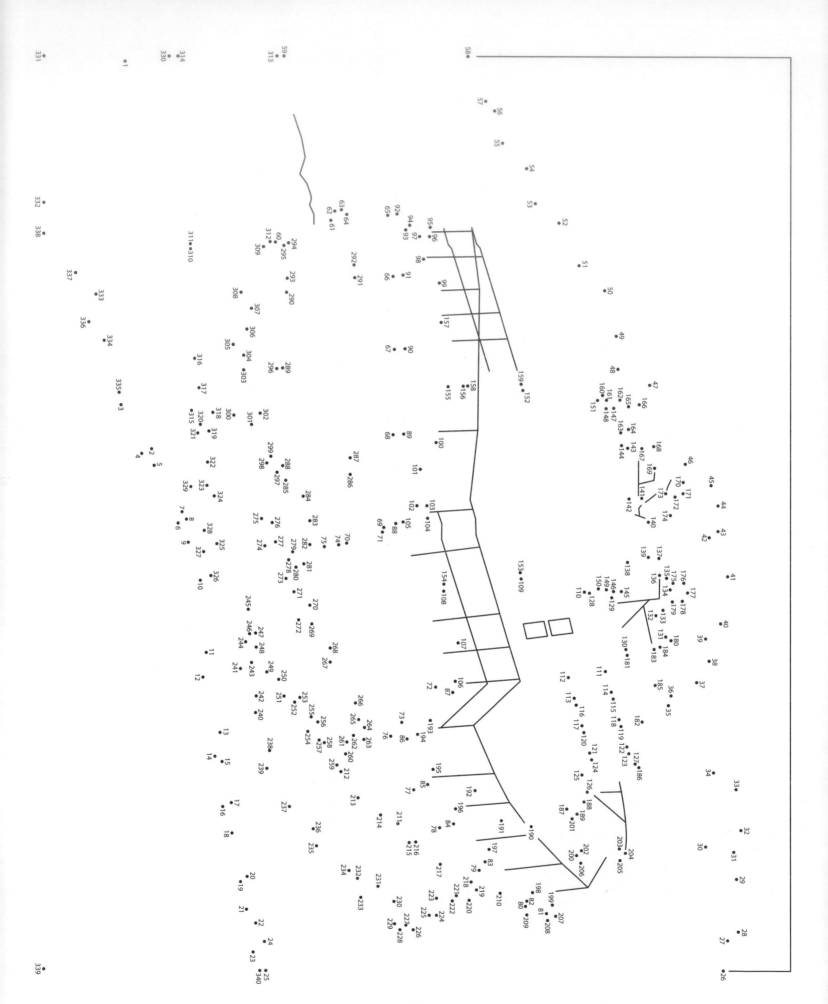

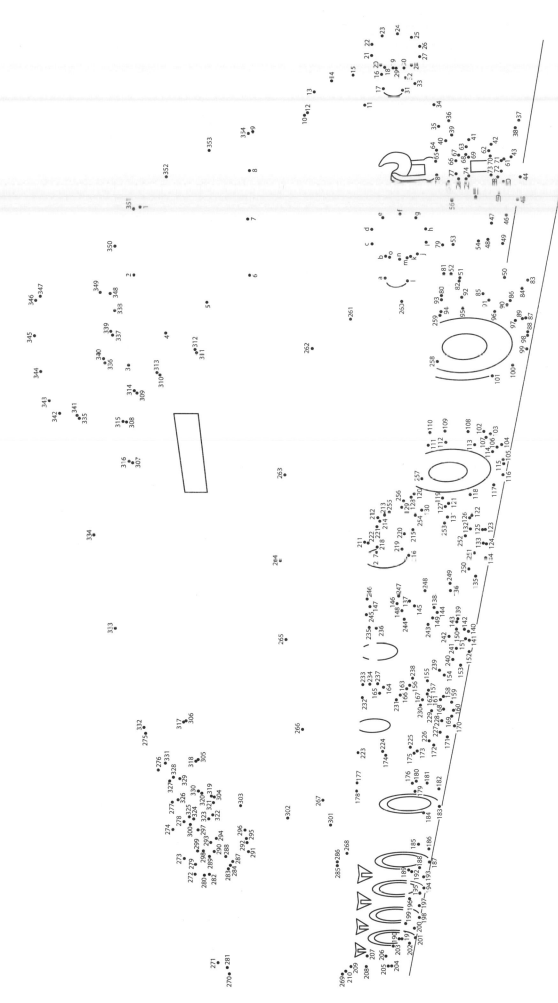

This picture is made from 2 continuous lines: a) numbers and b) lower case letters

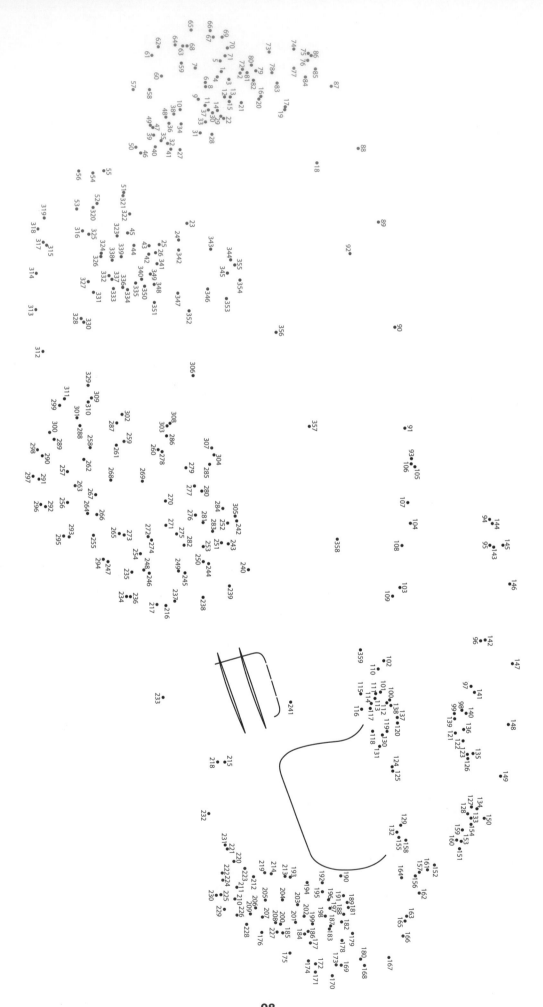

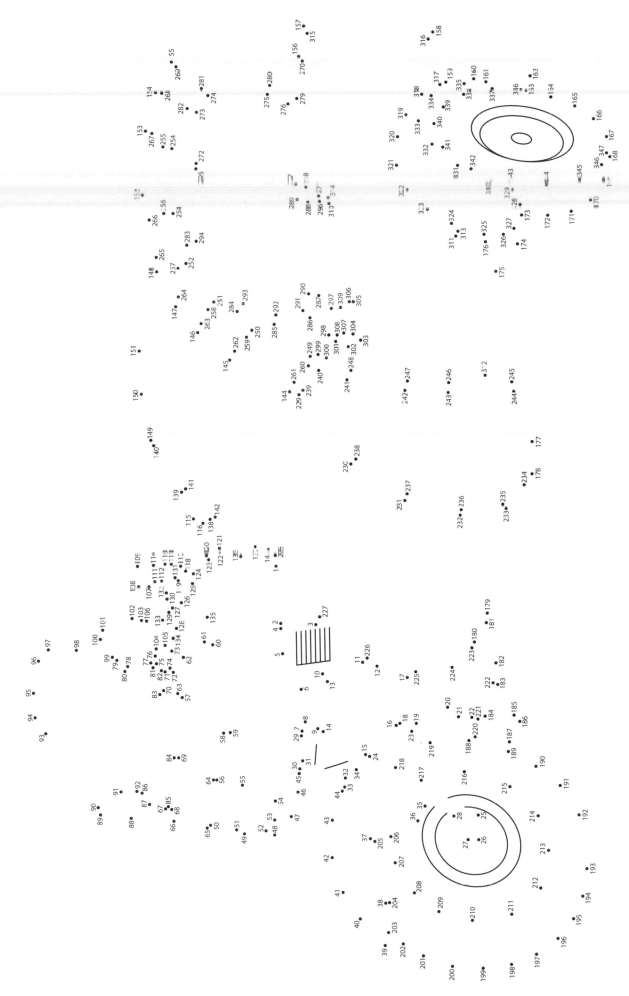

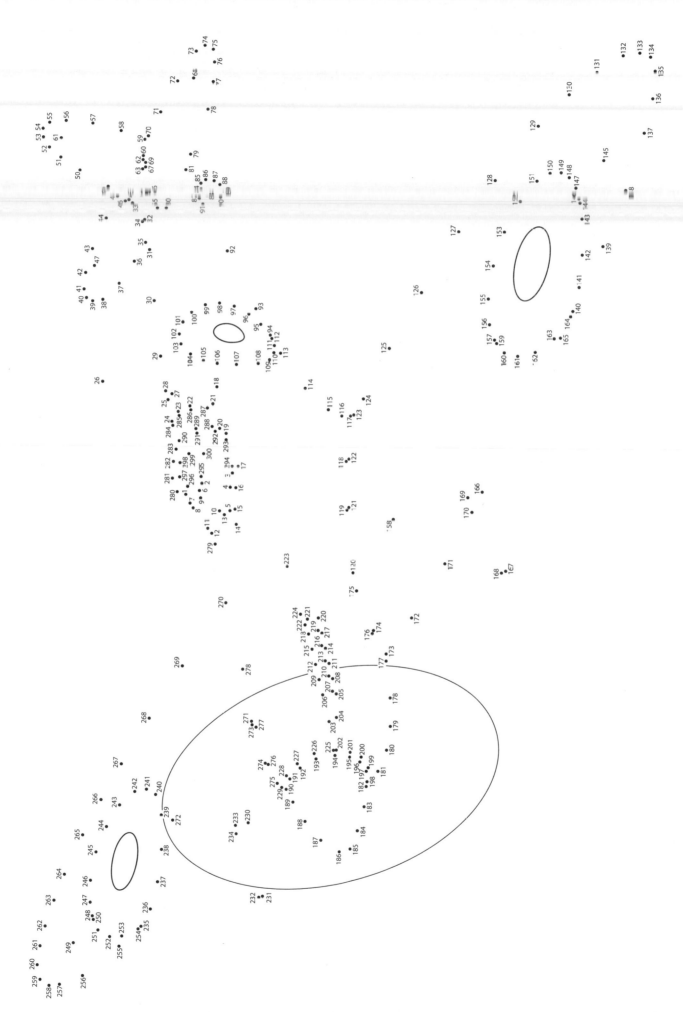

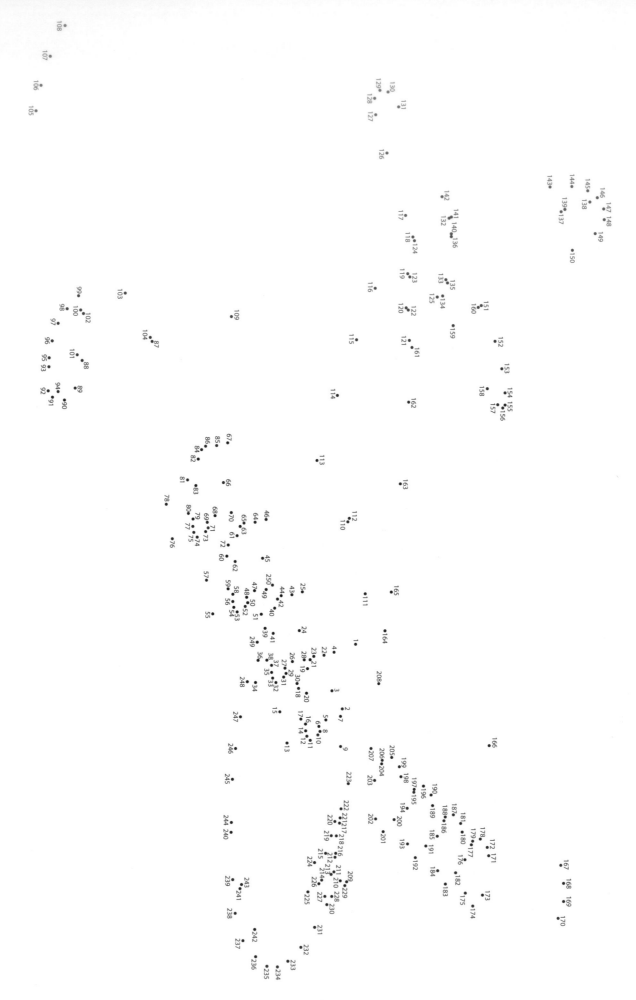

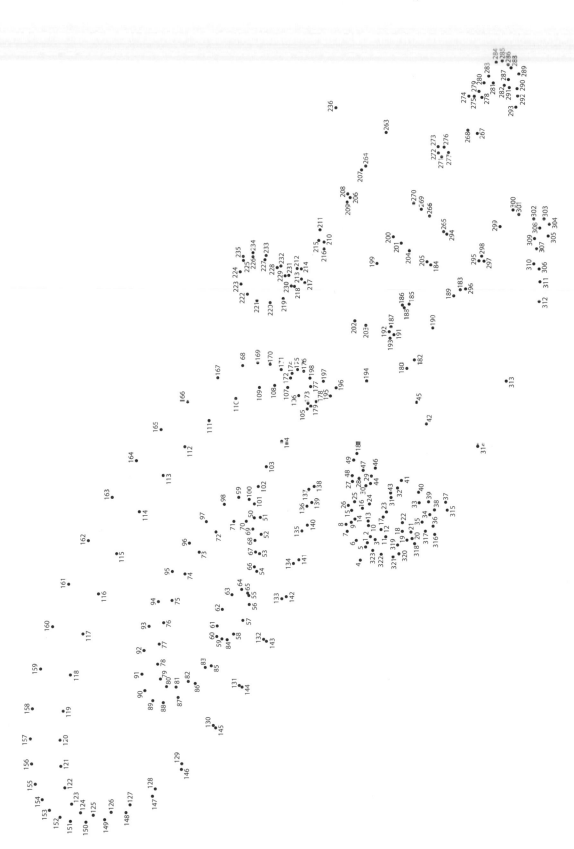

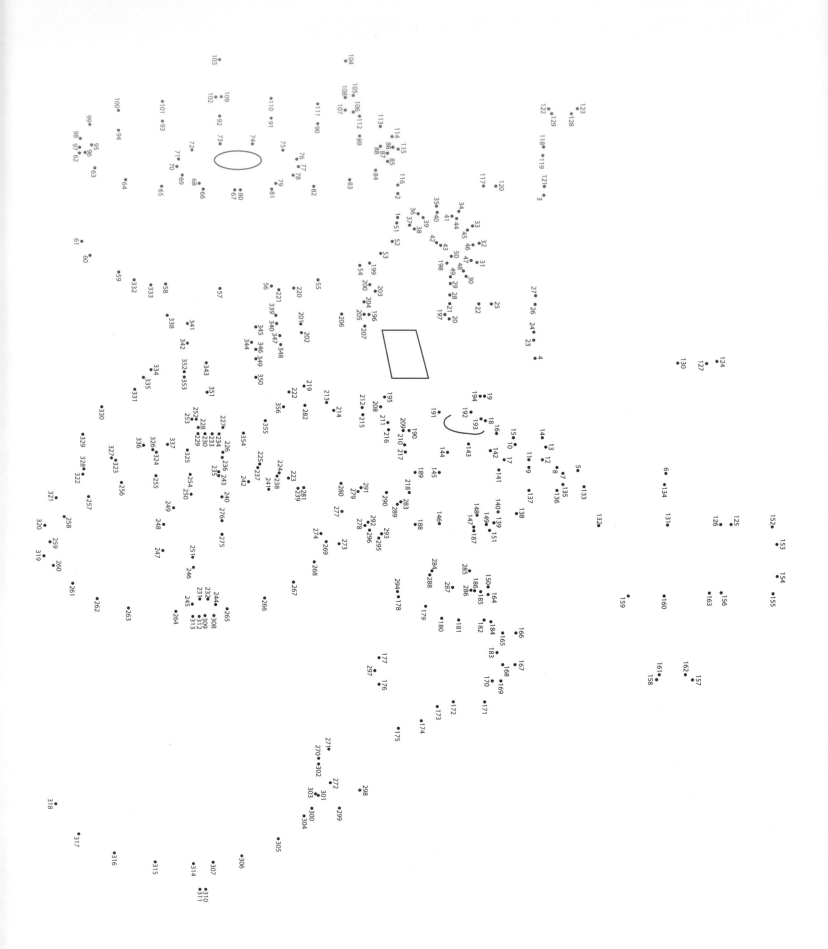

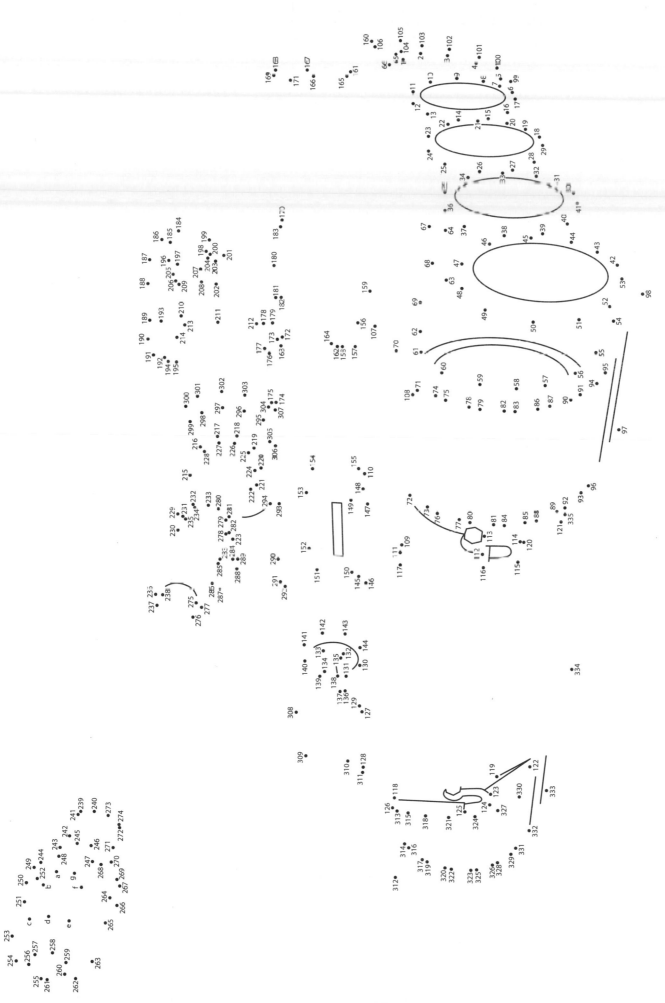

This picture is made from 2 continuous lines: a) numbers and b) lower case letters

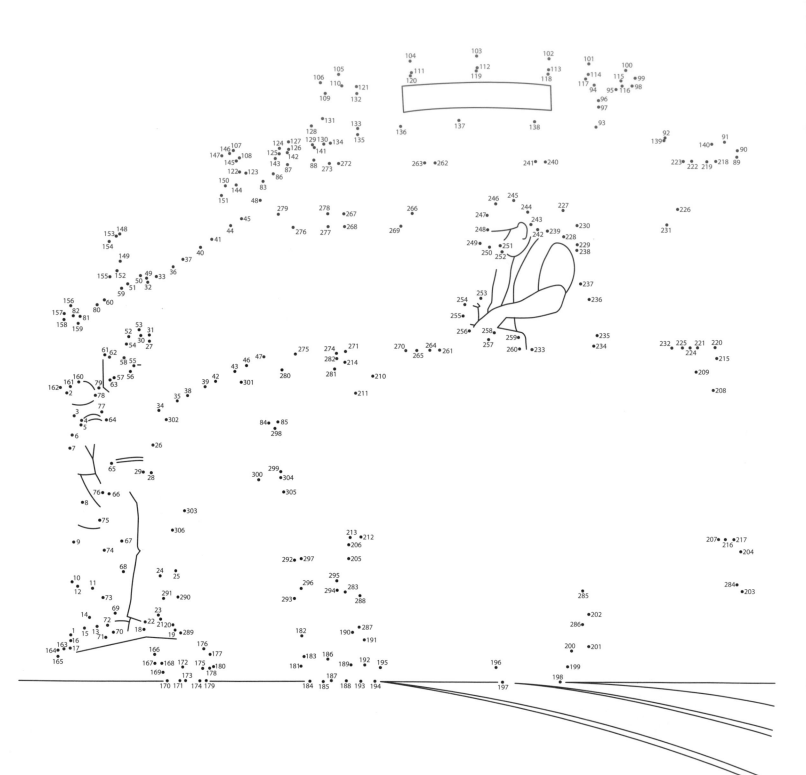

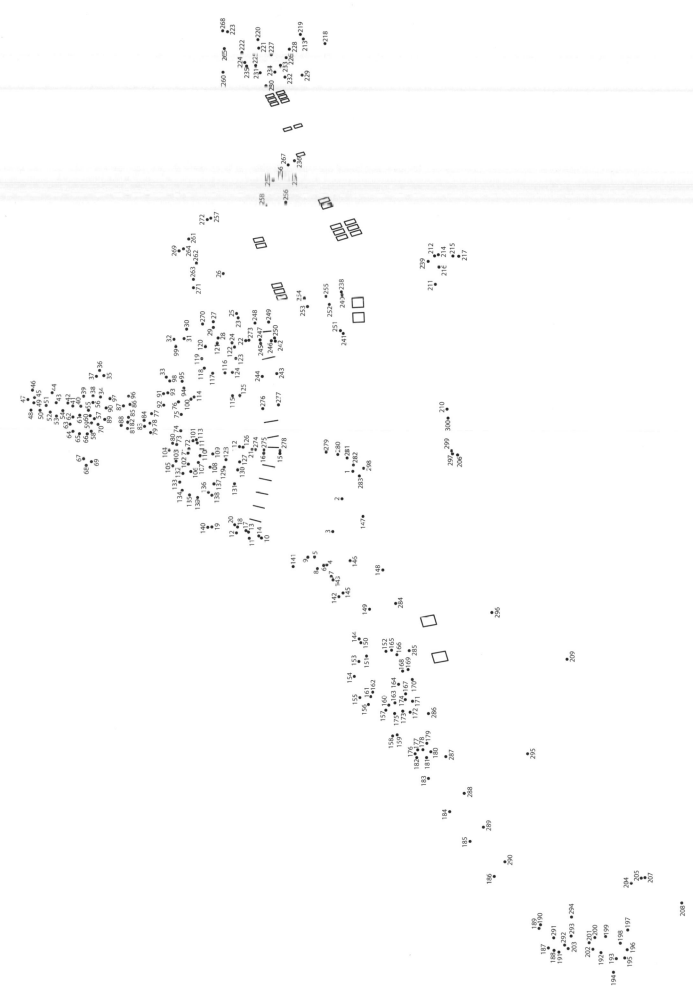

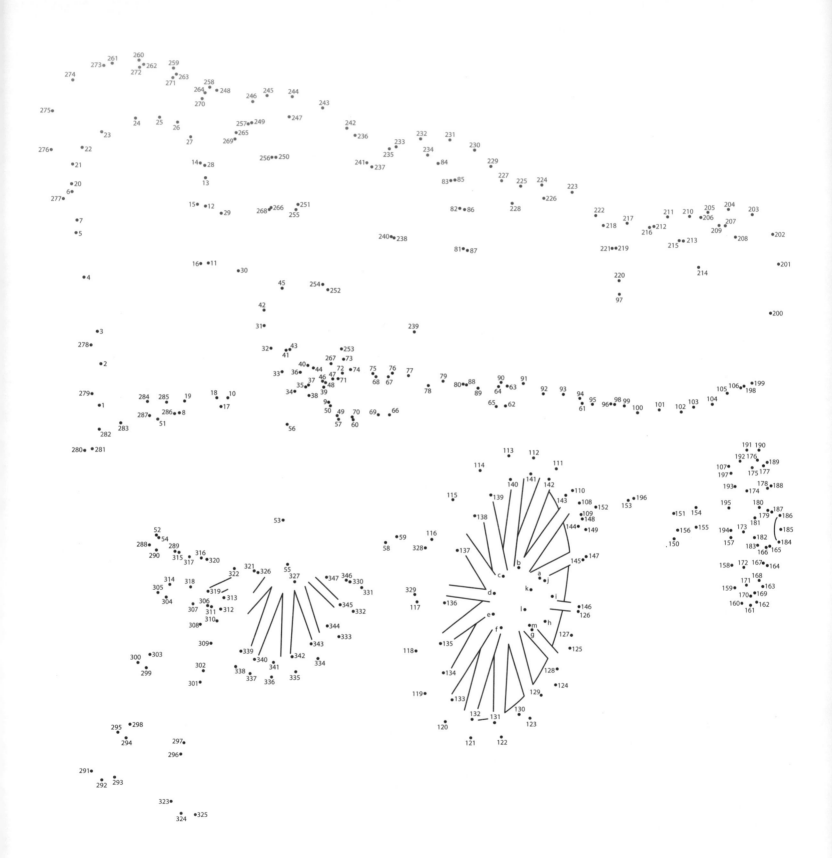

This picture is made from 2 continuous lines:
a) numbers and b) lower case letters

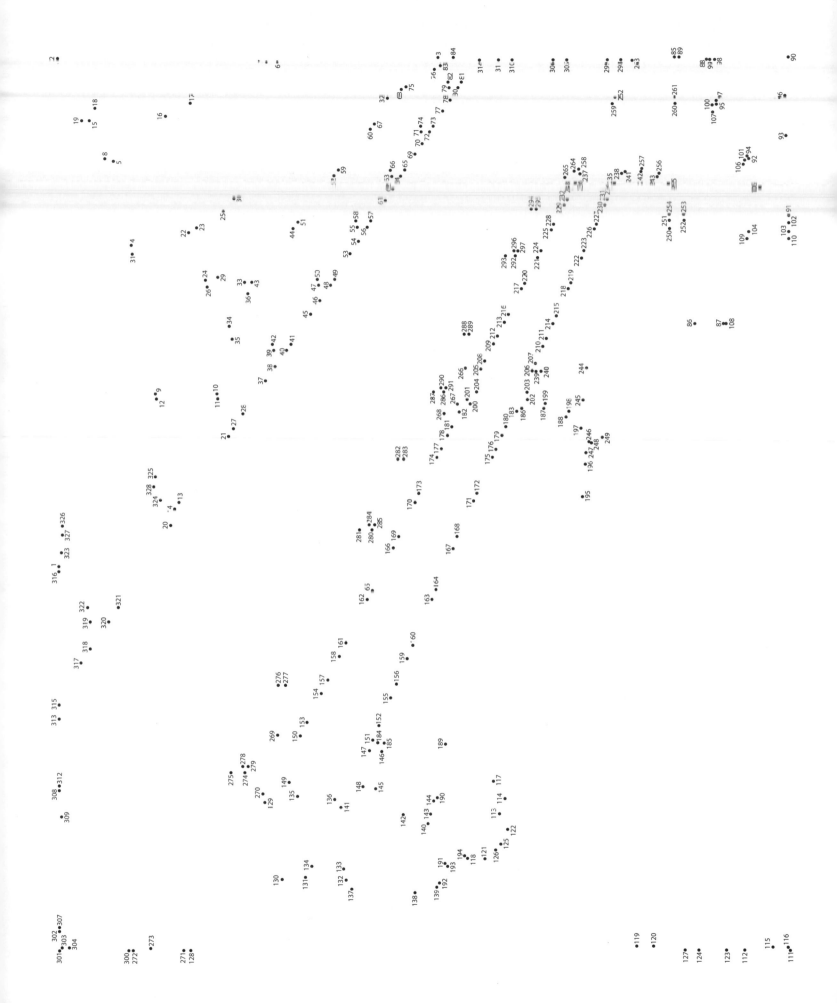

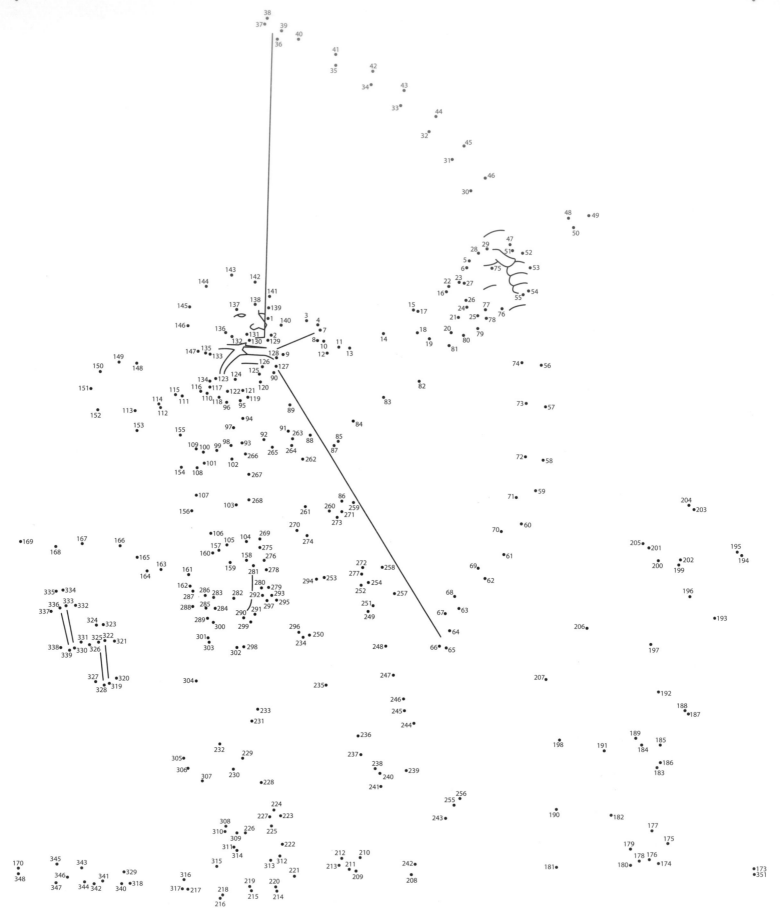

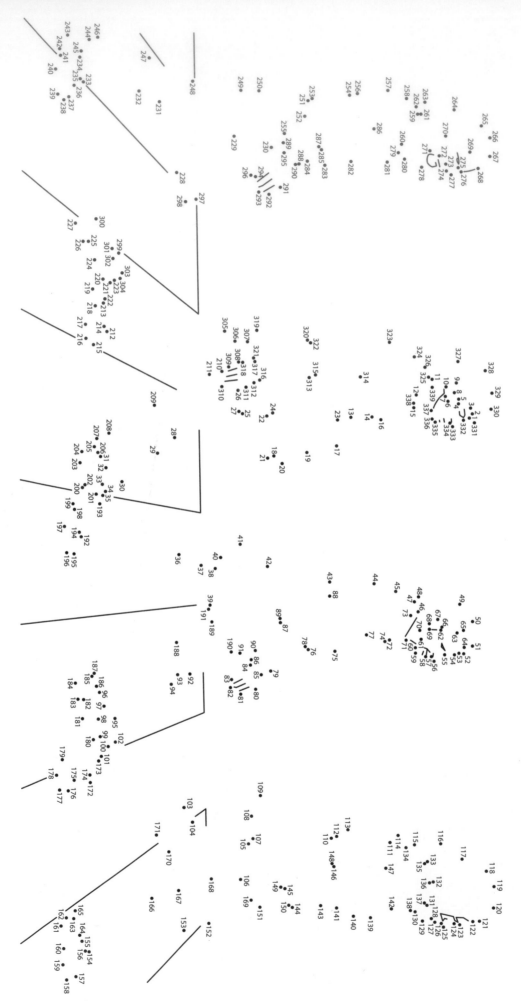

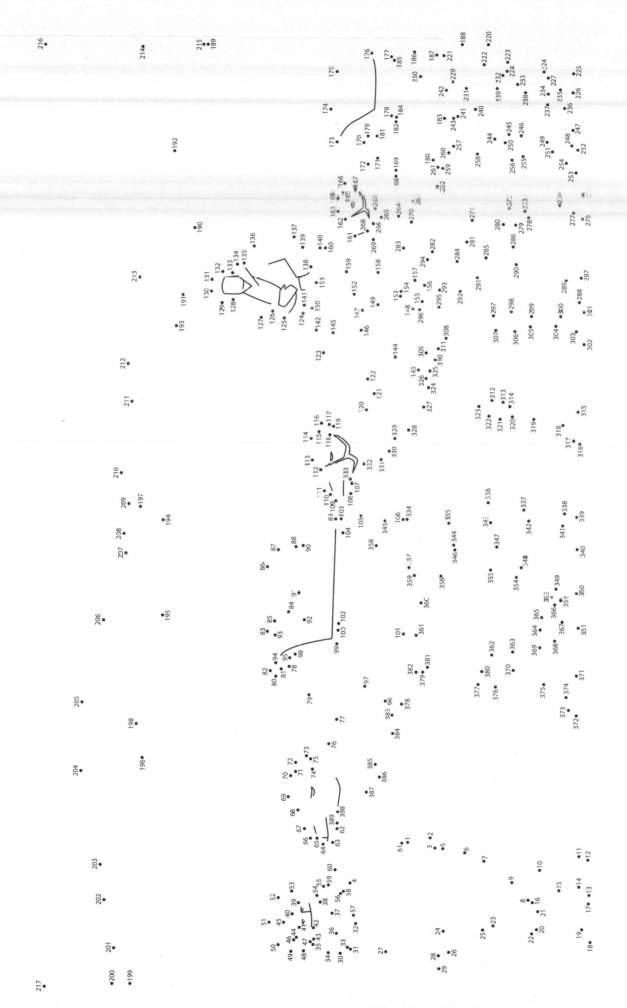

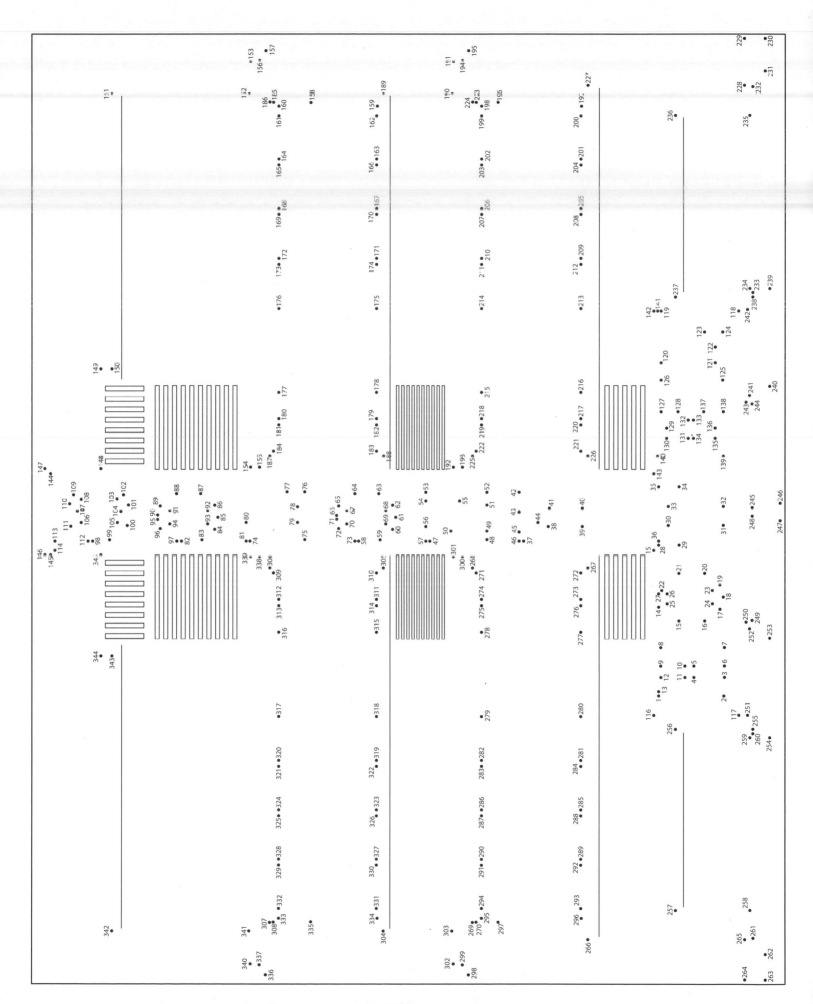

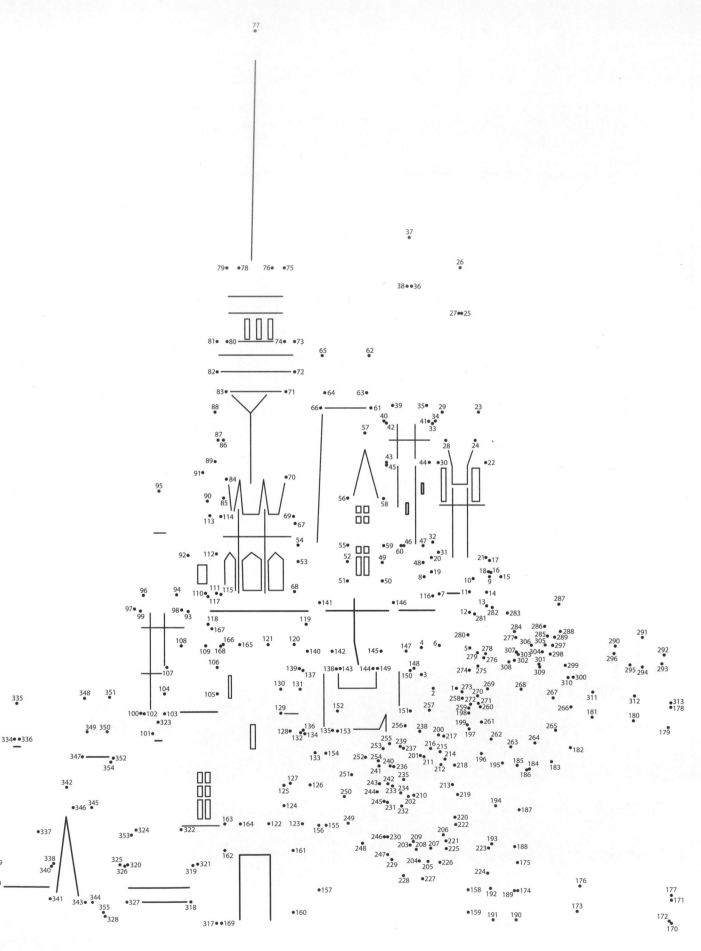

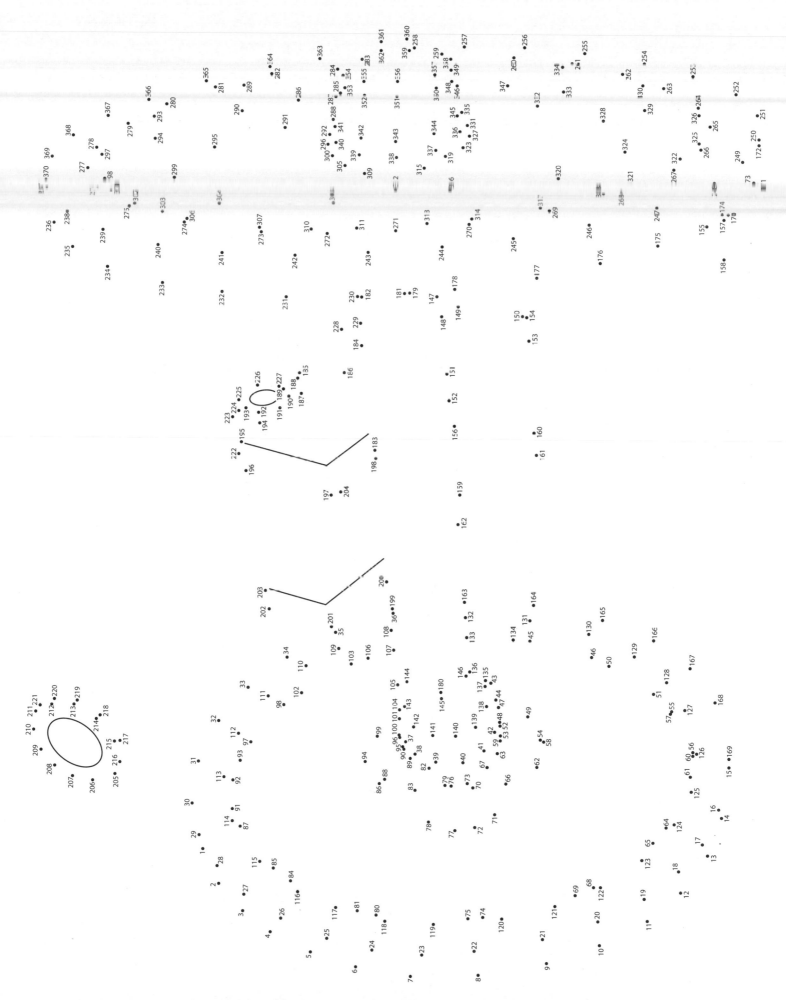

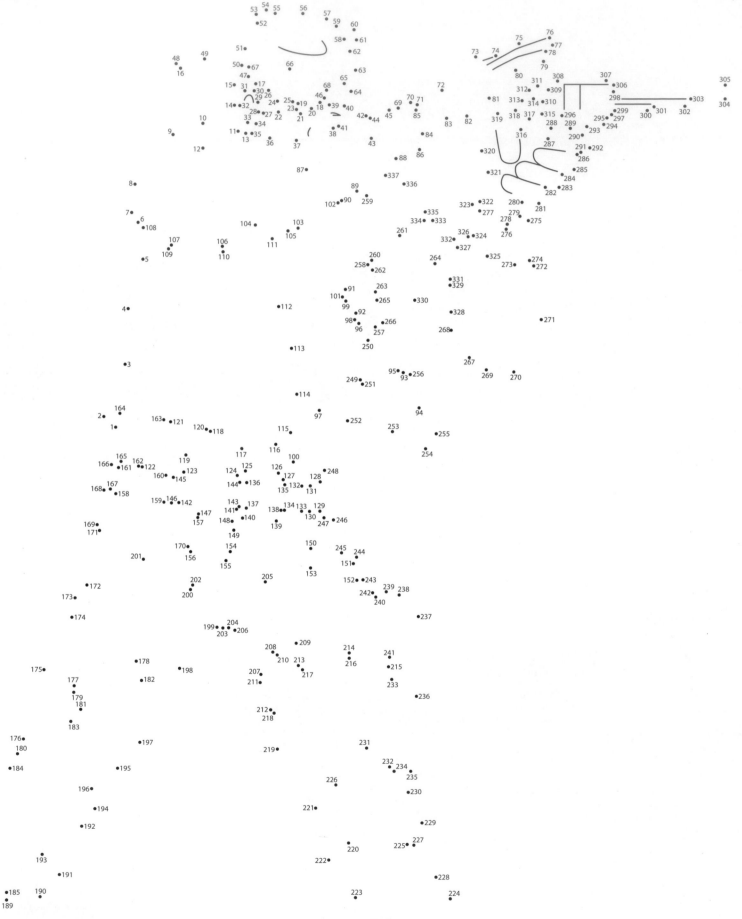

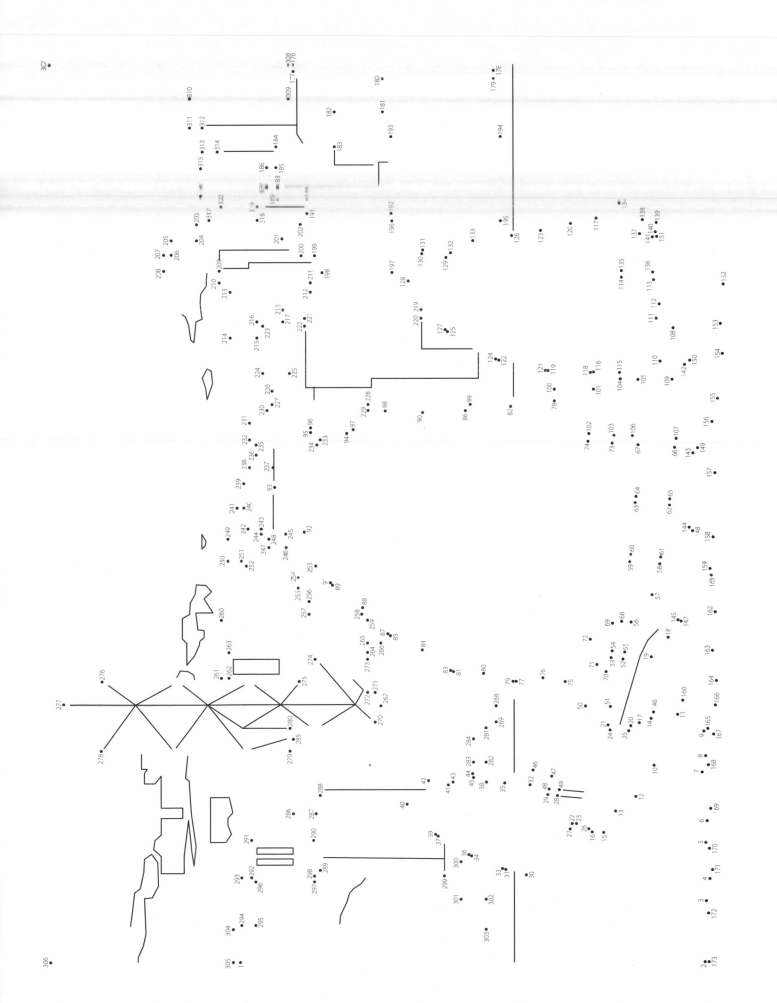

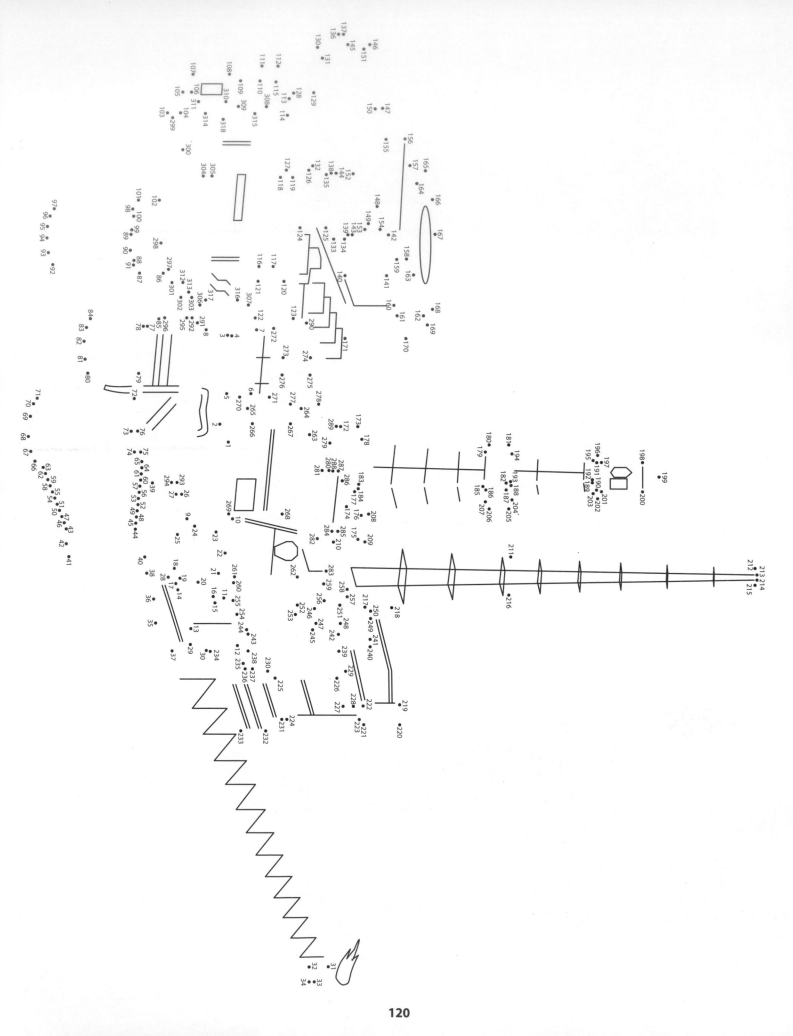

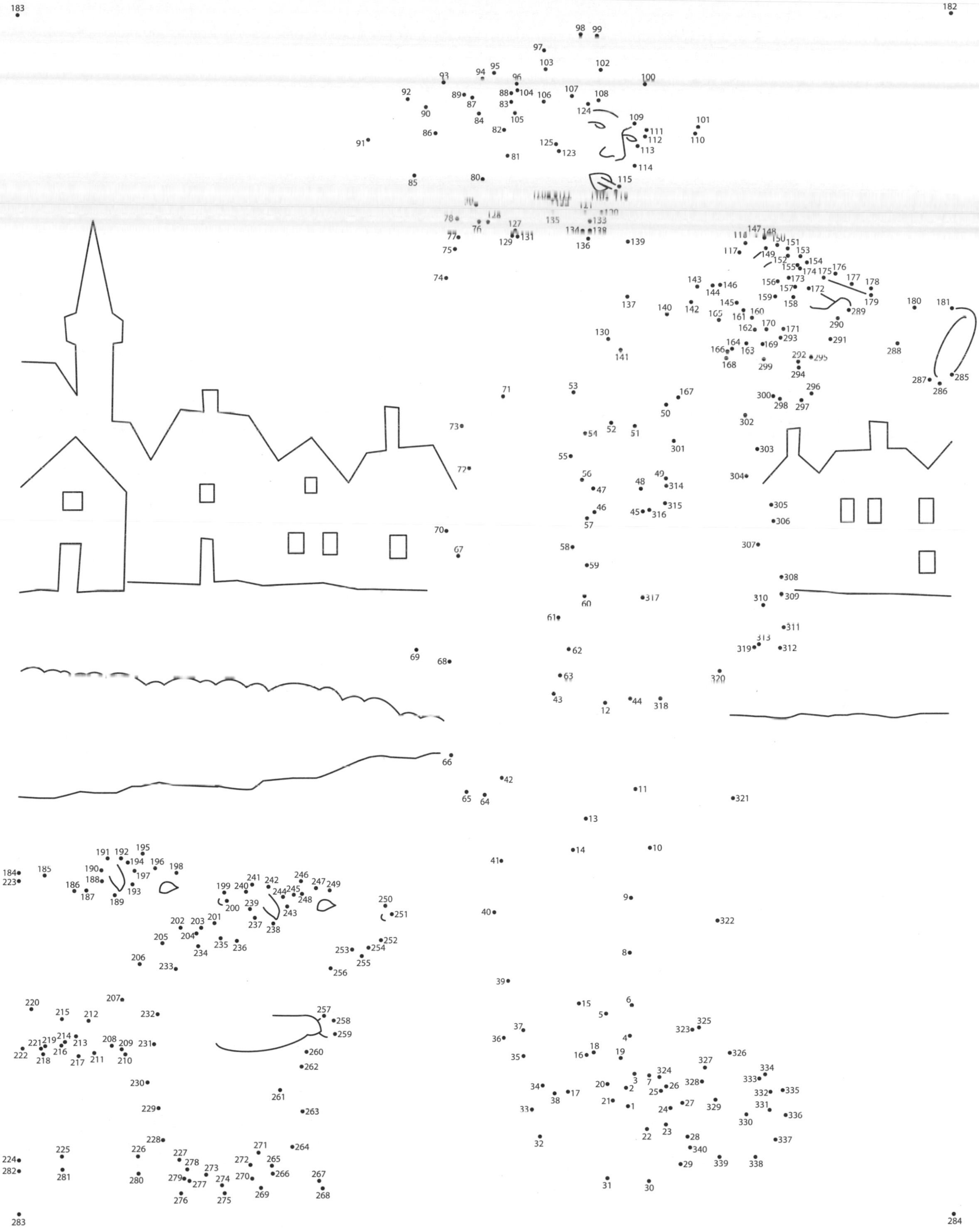

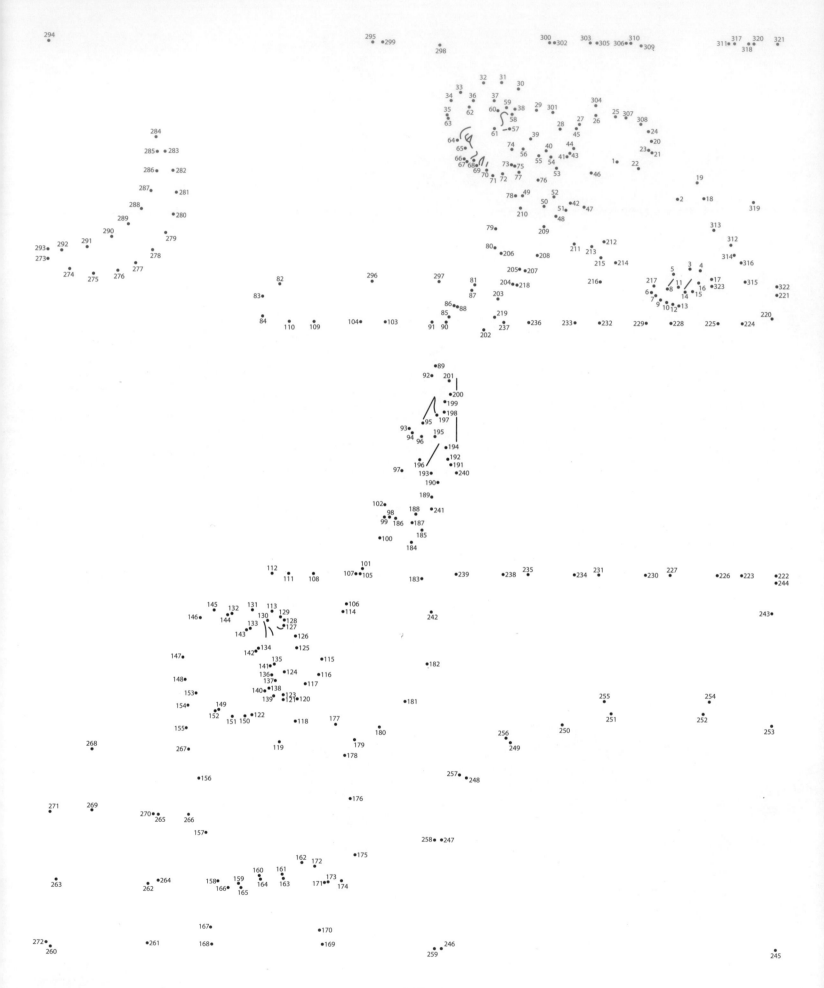

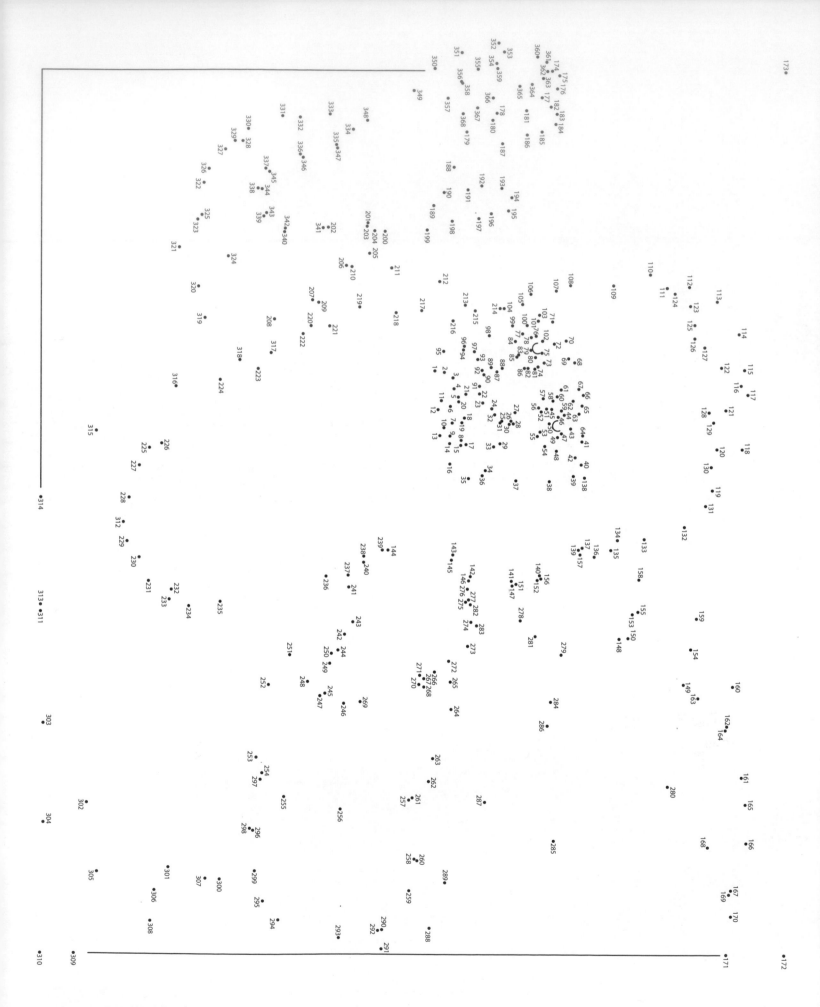

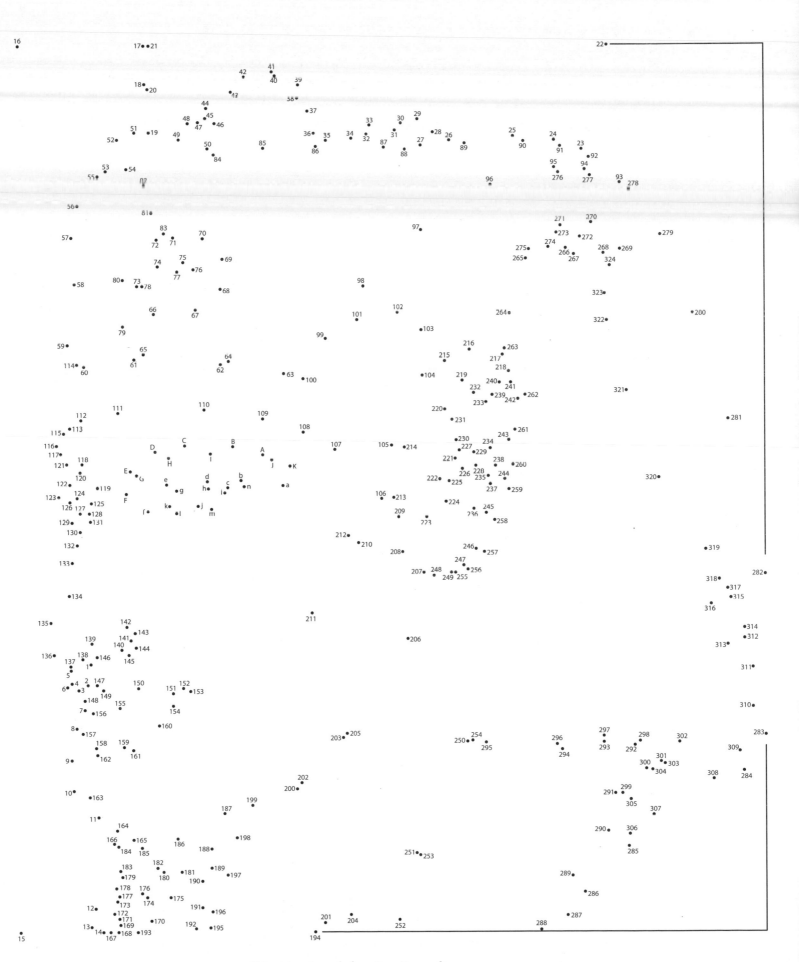

This picture is made from 3 continuous lines:
a) numbers, b) upper case letters and c) lower case letters

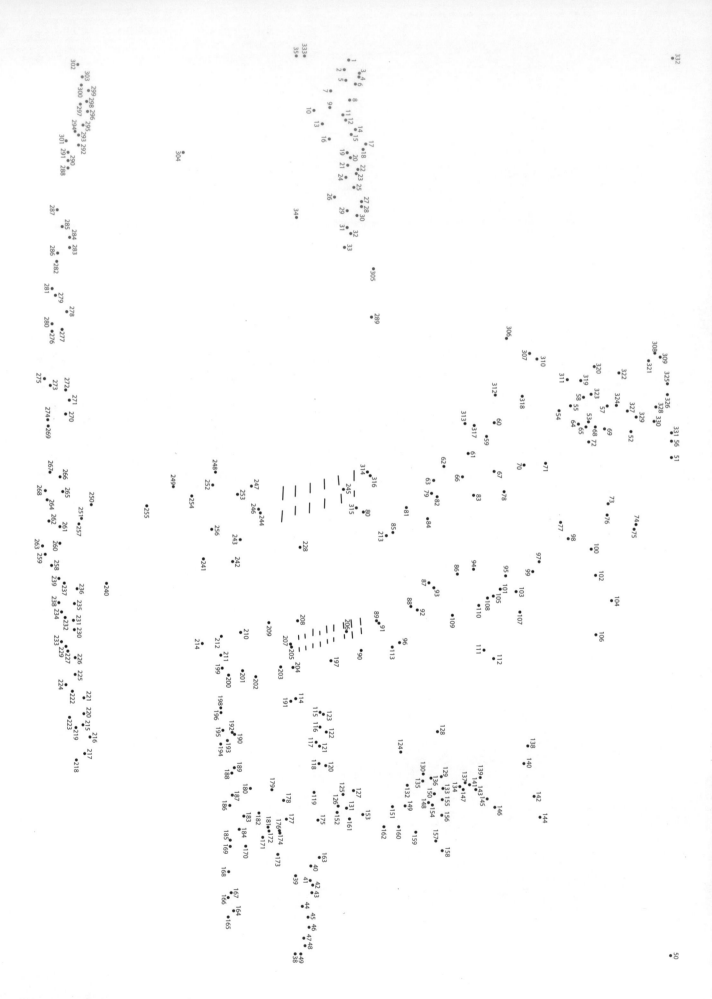

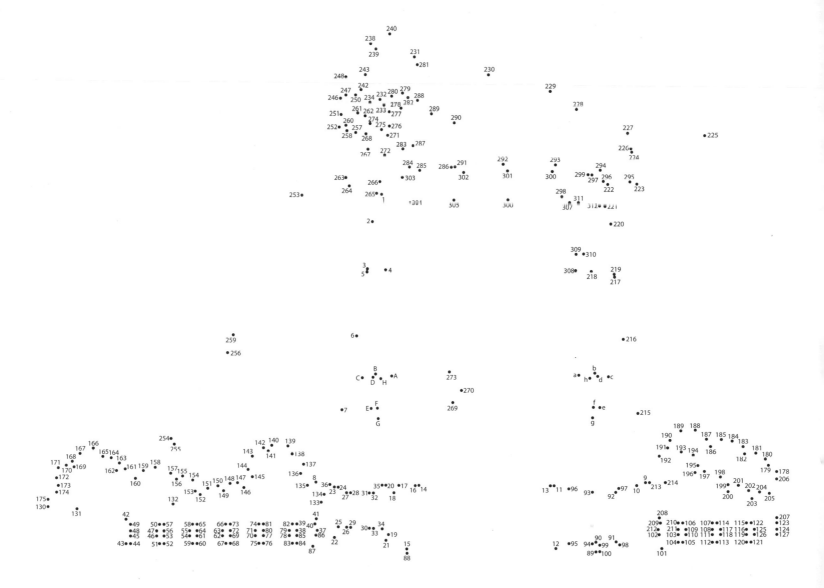

LIST OF ILLUSTRATIONS

THE ANIMAL KINGDOM
Elephant 7
Kangaroo, with baby 8
Meerkats 9
Owl in flight 10
Panda eating bamboo 11
Polar bear and cub 12
Penguins 13
Swans, courtship 14
Whale with calf 15

LANDMARKS
Alhambra, Granada 16
Brooklyn Bridge, New York 17
Burj Khalifa, Dubai 18
Capitol Building, Washington 19
Colonne de la Bastille, Paris 20
Little Mermaid, Copenhagen 21
London Eye, England 22
Mont St Michel, Normandy 23
Phare de Cordouan, France 24
Potala Palace, Tibet 25
The Shard, London 26
Tower Bridge, London 27
Zollverein coal mine industrial
   complex, Essen 28

ICONIC BUILDINGS
Astorga Episcopal Palace, Leon 29
Borgund Stave Church 30
Borobudur, Indonesia 31
Brighton Pavilion, England 32
Ca D'Oro, Venice 33
Duomo (Santa Maria del Fiore),
   Florence 34
Einstein Tower, Potsdam 35
Eltz Castle, Germany 36
Temple of the Emerald Buddha,
   Bangkok 37
Fontainebleau (horseshoe staircase) 38
Graumann's Chinese Theater,
   Los Angeles 39
Guggenheim Museum, New York 40
Nimes arena, France 41
Niteroi Contemporary Art Museum,
   Brazil 42
Notre Dame de Paris, France 43

Palais Garnier, Paris 44
Petit Hameau, Versailles 45
Royal Albert Hall, London 46
St Paul's Cathedral, London 47
San Xavier del Bac, Arizona 48
Speyer Cathedral, Germany 49
The Tower of London, England 50

WORKS OF ART
American Gothic (Grant Wood) 51
Arnolfini Marriage (Van Eyck) 52
Birth of Venus detail (Botticelli) 53
Statue of David (Michelangelo) 54
Girl with the Pearl Earring (Vermeer) 55
The Milkmaid (Vermeer) 56
Mr and Mrs Andrews (Gainsborough) 57
Sleep (Dali) 58
Sunflowers (Van Gogh) 59
Waterlilies (Monet) 60
Whistler's Mother 61

ENTERTAINMENT
Circus horse, performing 62
Clown 63
Christopher Lee as Dracula 64
Fender Stratocaster 65
Helter skelter 66
Humpty Dumpty 67
Charles Laughton as hunchback of
   Notre Dame 68
Ice skaters 69
Laurel and Hardy 70
Pas de deux 71
Punch and Judy 72
The Sound of Music 73
Tango 74
Tarzan 75

SPORT
Athlete on blocks 76
Racing catamaran 77
Synchronized diving 78
Formula One car 79
Golfer teeing off 80
Gymnast 81
Ice hockey 82
Moto GP 83

Pole vaulting 84
Quarterback 85
Scuba diver 86
Sculling 87
Show jumping 88
Sumo wrestlers 89
Water skiing 90
Windsurfing 91

AIR, LAND AND SEA
Bristol Boxkite 92
Concorde 93
Diving suit 94
Farm tractor 95
Lifeboat 96
Mallard class train engine 97
Mercedes 300L 98
Motorbike with sidecar 99
Pennyfarthing 100
Spitfire fighter plane 101
Spruce Goose 102
Star Trek space ship 103
Steamroller 104
German Tiger battle tank 105
Tram car 106
USS Independence 107
Covered wagon 108
Wuppertal suspended monorail 109

SCENES
Archer with long bow at Agincourt 110
Balinese mask 111
Beatles crossing Abbey Road, London 112
Camel train 113
Roman chariot 114
Colony Hotel, Florida 115
Disneyland, Florida 116
Gettysburg cannon 117
Gunfighter 118
Hong Kong harbour 119
Oil rig 120
Pied Piper of Hamelin 121
Romeo & Juliet 122
Samurai warrior 123
Father Christmas 124
Egyptian Sphinx 125
Teepees 126
Dutch windmill 127